Worship & Praise

Songbook

Augsburg Fortress
Minneapolis

Contents

Worship & Praise
Songbook

Also available:
Worship & Praise Full Music Edition (3-851) ISBN 0-8066-3851-6
Worship & Praise compact disc (3-852) ISBN 0-8066-3852-4

The paper used in this publication meets the minimum requirements of American National Standard for Information Sciences—Permanence of Paper for Printed Materials, ANSI Z329.48-1984.
Printed in the USA.

Manufactured in the U.S.A. ISBN 0-8066-3850-8 3-850

09 08 07 06 05 04 03 02 3 4 5 6 7 8 9 10 11 12 13 14 15 16 17 18 19 20

Welcome . . .

to the *Worship & Praise* Songbook, a collection of carefully selected songs of the Christian faith, suitable for use in worship and at other times. Here are songs of adoration and praise, prayer and lament, thanksgiving and trust, justice and joy. Here are brief choruses and refrains, songs that tell a story, songs that use warm and personal faith language, well-loved Bible verses set to music, classic texts of Christian worship set to new rhythms and melodies. Here are songs for many times and seasons of the church's year and the Christian's life.

Many congregations are supplementing their repertoire of congregational song with worship songs such as these, blending the richness of the church's tradition with the freshness of more recent expressions in words and music. Since no single volume could contain the many songs that have emerged in the last generation, one goal of this collection is to present a sampling of the most widely used and the most broadly useful songs for congregations at worship in the first years of the 21st century. Talented song writers have added a limited number of new materials as well. Contemporary music and worship leaders, pastors, and theologians have graciously assisted worship staff members of the publisher and of the Division for Congregational Ministries of the Evangelical Lutheran Church in America in selecting and carefully reviewing the words and music of these songs.

Worship & Praise Songbook contains core materials for worshiping assemblies: the words and a single melody line for each song. Basic chord symbols are also provided. A few songs often sung in harmony are included as four-part arrangements. The songs are ordered alphabetically by their common titles for ease in locating them. Indexes of topics, themes, and scripture references identify songs suitable for particular seasons and occasions. Copyright information appears at the end of each song, with more details in an appendix, to simplify obtaining permission for reproducing in any form the words and/or music of a song.

Worship & Praise Full Music Edition is an essential companion to the Songbook. Keyboard players, guitarists, percussionists, and other ensemble musicians will find the full musical arrangement of each song in this volume, including keyboard score and complete chord symbols. Drum kit patterns are contained in an appendix, along with a musical key index. Pastors, musicians, and worship planners will find the section "Using *Worship & Praise*" and the expanded indexes to be helpful tools for using these songs within basic patterns of worship. A recording of selected songs from *Worship & Praise* is available separately as a tool for those who learn and lead this music.

In the astounding diversity of worship, God's people on earth participate even now in the vision of Revelation 5: in the assembly of ". . . a great multitude that no one could count from every nation, from all tribes and peoples and languages, standing before the throne and before the Lamb, with palm branches in their hands." May these songs in musical languages of our day add to the breadth of the church's timeless song.

A song of unity

C Dm G
As a moth - er hen gath - ers her chicks, as an ea - gle
C Am
lifts up her young, you have called to your ta - ble all
Dm C/G G C Fine
peo - ple as one; God, we thank you for your pres - ence here.
Dm G
As we share in the bread and the wine, come to us, ho - ly
C Am
Je - sus, in love. Let the gift of your sac - ri - fice
Dm C/G G G7 C D.C. al fine
o - pen our eyes; we are one in your bo - dy and blood.

Text and music: David M. Jahn

2 A story for all people

G2
D/F♯
1 As peo - ple wait in dark - ness, in
2 We come in - to your pres - ence, in
3 A time of prep - a - ra - tion: the
4 You call us to re - pen - tance, to
5 Re - newed by this en - coun - ter, we'll
Em7
Asus
A7
F♯m7
fear of end - less night, send forth your word of
hope and joy re - stored. With ea - ger hearts we
guest is draw - ing near, as moun - tain plac - es
turn and start a - gain. You send your Ho - ly
go out and pro - claim. We'll tell of your sal -
A/B
Bm
G
F♯7sus
F♯7
com - fort, a mes - sage of great light. The
lis - ten, and gath - er 'round your word. We
crum - ble and straight - ened paths ap - pear. Pre -
Spir - it to drown the pow'r of sin. We
va - tion, and mag - ni - fy your name. The
Bm
Bm/A
G
D/F♯
Em
world stands proud be - fore you, con - flict - ed, hun - gry,
watch and wait your com - ing, and pray for great - er
pare a hum - ble wel - come in ev - 'ry heart and
won - der in your mer - cy, your sing - ing fes - tal
ser - vant words of Mar - y will swell the faith - ful

A7sus A7 G F♯ Bm F♯m/A Bm
poor. Come, scat - ter pride and fool - ish - ness, and
trust, to know that while we wait for you, Em -
home, and cel - e - brate the prom - ise of our
voice; and in your meal of bread and wine we
soul, and you will bring your chil - dren home that
Em F♯m7 G A G/D
mend all souls with Sav - ior love once more.
man - u - el, you watch and wait with us.
God who is, and was, and is to come.
join the in - vi - ta - tion to re - joice!
day when all cre - a - tion will be whole.
Refrain
D G A/G F♯m7 B Em A
A sto - ry for all peo - ple, old sto - ry new to -
Am6/C B7 Em A F♯m7 Bm
day. A song of love and heal - ing, a
Em F♯m Em/G A7 G/D D
light to show the way.

Text: Dori Erwin Collins
Music: Dori Erwin Collins; arr. Daniel Kallman

All hail King Jesus

F/A C/G F C/E C C/E B♭/F F
All hail King Je - sus! All hail Em - man - u - el,
A/E Dm Dm/B G7 Gm C
King of kings, Lord of lords, bright Morn - ing Star.
B♭/C C F FM7/E F7/E♭ 3 B♭/D B♭ Gm7(♭5)
And through - out e - ter - ni - ty, I'll sing your prais - es;
F/C Dm7 Gm7 B♭/C C7 F B♭/F F
and I'll reign with you through - out e - ter - ni - ty.

Text and music: Dave Moody

All is ready now

D B9sus Bm
1 Qui - et - ly in - to the sta - ble where the
2 'Cross the thresh - old of cre - a - tion, Je - sus
3 Now en - throned as king of heav - en, blaz - ing
Em Asus A7 G
Sav - ior sleep - ing lies, we can go, for all are
comes to dwell with us, as he was in the be -
glo - ry like the sun: in his hands are pow'r and
D/F♯ E9sus E7
wel - come: shep - herd, an - gel, poor, and
gin - ning, ev - er - more God's gift of
jus - tice, on his lips are peace and
Asus A7 D D/F♯ A/G G
wise. What we have we bring and of - fer, earth - ly
love. Now he calls us to the ta - ble, gift of
love. As our gifts are turned to ash - es, fall - ing
Bm E Em
gifts for Child di - vine, giv - ing that which we were
love to bleed and die; man - ger here be - comes an
down in awe we bow, emp - ty - hand - ed, we a -
D/F♯ G6 A7sus D
giv - en, fruits of har - vest, bread and wine.
al - tar, sta - ble Lamb is sac - ri - ficed.
dore him. "Come, for all is read - y now."

Text and music: Jay Beech

5
All that we have
Refrain
E♭ Gm A♭ E♭
All that we have and all that we of - fer comes from a
Gm A♭ E♭ A♭ E♭
heart both fright - ened and free. Take what we bring now and
Cm Gm A♭ E♭
give what we need, all done in your name.
Cm Gm
1 Some would re - ly on their pow - er,
2 Some - times the road may be lone - some,
3 Some - times when trou - bles are man - y,
A♭ Cm/G
oth - ers put trust in their gold.
of - ten we may lose our way. Take
life can seem emp - ty, it's true. But
Fm Cm
Some have on - ly their Sav - ior, whose
cour - age and al - ways re - mem - ber
look at the life of the Mas - ter, who
Fm Gm A♭6 B♭sus B♭
Refrain
faith - ful - ness nev - er grows old.
love is - n't just for a day.
lov - ing - ly suf - fered for you.

Text: Gary Ault
Music: Gary Ault; arr. Gary Daigle

Alleluia

G C Am7 D C/G G
1 Al - le - lu - ia, al - le - lu - ia, al - le - lu - ia, al - le - lu - ia;
2 He's my Sav - ior, al - le - lu - ia, he's my Sav - ior, al - le - lu - ia;
3 He is wor - thy, al - le - lu - ia, he is wor - thy, al - le - lu - ia;
4 I will praise him, al - le - lu - ia, I will praise him, al - le - lu - ia;
G C Am7 D C/G G
al - le - lu - ia, al - le - lu - ia, al - le - lu - ia, al - le - lu - ia.
he's my Sav - ior, al - le - lu - ia, he's my Sav - ior, al - le - lu - ia.
he is wor - thy, al - le - lu - ia, he is wor - thy, al - le - lu - ia.
I will praise him, al - le - lu - ia, I will praise him, al - le - lu - ia.

Text and music: Jerry Sinclair

Alleluia. Lord, to whom shall we go?

F C/E Gm7 C C/B♭ F/A
Al-le-lu-ia. Lord, to whom shall we go? You have the
B♭ C Dm F/A B♭2 Csus
words of e-ter-nal life. Al-le-lu-ia.
Dm Gm7 C7sus C F/A B♭ C F
Al-le-lu-ia, al-le-lu-ia. Al-le-
F/A B♭2 Csus Dm Gm7 C7sus C F
lu-ia. Al-le-lu-ia, al-le-lu-ia.

Text: John 6:68, adapt. *Lutheran Book of Worship*
Music: Robin Cain; arr. Phil Kadidlo

Amazing love

C
Dm7
Gsus
G
1 My Lord, what love is this that pays so
2 And so they watched him die, de - spised, re -
3 And now this love of Christ shall flow like
Csus
F/G
dear - ly, that I, the guilt - y one, may go free?
ject - ed; but, oh, the blood he shed flowed for me.
riv - ers; come, wash your guilt a - way, live a - gain.
Refrain
Gm7
E♭
A - maz - ing love, oh, what sac - ri - fice, the Son of God giv'n for
me; my debt he pays and my death he dies, that
I might live, that I might live.

Text and music: Graham Kendrick

As the deer

D A/C♯ Bm Bm/A G Asus A D
As the deer pants for the wa-ter, so my soul longs af-ter you.
A/C♯ Bm D/A D/F♯ Em7 A7sus A7 D
You a-lone are my heart's de-sire and I long to wor-ship you.
Bm Bm/A G D/F♯ G Bm/F♯ Em F♯sus F♯
You a-lone are my strength, my shield, to you a-lone may my spir-it yield;
D A/C♯ Bm D/A D/F♯ Em7 A7sus A7 D
you a-lone are my heart's de-sire, and I long to wor-ship you.

Text and music: Martin J. Nystrom

As the grains of wheat

Refrain
F Eb/F Bb/F F C/E
As the grains of wheat once scat - tered on the hill were
Dm Am Gm7 C sus C
gath - ered in - to one, were gath - ered in - to one to be -
Eb9 Bb/D Gm7 F/A
come our bread; so may all your peo - ple from the
Bb G/B C sus C Eb Bb/D Bb/C C Eb/F Bb/F F
ends of the earth be gath - ered in - to one in you.
Eb/F F Eb/F F
1 As this cup of bless - ing is shared with - in our midst,
2 Let this be a fore - taste of all that is to. . . . come,
Refrain
Gm7 F/A Eb Bb/C C sus C
may we share in the pres - ence of your ten - der love.
when all cre - a - tion. . . will share. . . in the feast with you.

Text: Didache, 2nd cent., refrain; Marty Haugen, stanzas
Music: David Haas

11 At the foot of the cross

C F2 Gsus C F2
At the foot of the cross, I can hard - ly take it in,
Gsus Am G C/E F
that the King of all cre - a - tion was
Am F/A Gsus G C/E F2
dy - ing for my sin; and the pain and ag - o - ny,
Gsus C/E F2 Gsus
and the thorns that pierced your head, and the
Am G Em7 F C/E C Am7 F2/A
hard - ness of my sin - ful heart that left you there for dead.
Gsus G Am G/A F C
And, oh, what mer - cy I have found at the

Am G/A C/G F Am G/A
cross of Cal - va - ry; I will nev - er know your lone -
F Am C/G F2/G G7sus G7
li - ness, all on ac - count of me. And I will
Am G/A F C Am G/A C/G
bow my knee be - fore your throne, 'cause your love has set me
F Am G/A F C/E
free; and I will give my life to you, dear Lord, and
Dm7 F G G/B Am Dm7 F
praise your maj - es - ty, and praise your
G G/B Am F G C
maj - es - ty, and praise your maj - es - ty.

Text and music: Derek Bond

At the name of Jesus

Refrain
D2 Bm7 G2 D2 Bm7 G2
At the name of Je - sus, at the name of Je - sus.
G2 Em7 Bm7 G A2
1 Ev-'ry knee shall bow in the heav-ens and earth, and ev-'ry
2 Ev-'ry tongue con-fess that Je-sus Christ . . . is Lord, ... to the
Em7 Bm7 GM7 Em7 A G2
Refrain
tongue con-fess that Je - sus is Lord, he is Lord!
glo-ry of God, to the glo-ry of God the . . . Fa-ther.
Final refrain
D2 Bm7 G2 D2 Bm7 G2 D2
At the name of Je - sus, at the name of Je - sus.

Text: Philippians 2:10-11, adapt. Richard Webb
Music: Richard Webb

Awesome God

Em C G/B G
Our God is an awe - some God, he
D Em D/E Em C
reigns from heav - en a - bove with wis - dom,
G/B G Am Em/B Bm7 Em
pow'r, and love— our God is an awe - some God!
Am Em/B Bm7 Em Am7 Em/B Bm7 Em
Our God is an awe - some God! Our God is an awe - some God!

Text and music: Rich Mullins

14

Baptized and set free

D C2 G A

1 We are peo - ple cre - a - ted, cho - sen by God.
2 We are fed and we're nour - ished, filled and re - freshed.
3 We are nour - ished by wa - ter, all liv - ing things,
4 Now with praise and thanks - giv - ing, we join the song.

D C2 G A

Then we're washed, ev - er gent - ly, in mer - cy and love.
Then our hun - ger re - turns and a - gain we are blessed.
and by life that the Spir - it a - bun - dant - ly brings.
All are wel - come! We gath - er to sing loud and strong.

Bm F♯m G A

Sin has pow - er no more. Je - sus o - pened the door
For what - ev - er the need, God is great - er in - deed:
As we jour - ney toward home, may your pres - ence be known:
Not en - slaved, but set free! From now on, all will be

Bm G A D

to a Foun - tain bring - ing heal - ing, and whole - ness and more.
end - less O - cean, al - ways deep - er than all of our need.
pre - cious Riv - er, ev - er - flow - ing, now car - ry us home.
one in Je - sus, one in wa - ter, bap - tized and set free!

Text and music: Cathy Skogen-Soldner

Be bold, be strong

B♭
A♭2
E♭
Be bold, be strong, for the Lord your God is with
B♭
A♭2
E♭
you. Be bold, be strong, for the Lord your God is with
B♭
E♭
F
Gm
E♭
F
Gm
you. Do not be a - fraid, do not be dis - mayed.
E♭
F
Gm
Walk in faith and vic - to - ry,
E♭
F
Gm
E♭
F
Gm
walk in faith and vic - to - ry, walk in faith and vic -
F
E♭
F
Cm/B♭
B♭
- to - ry, for the Lord your God is with you.

Text and music: Morris Chapman

Be my home

F
Dm7
B♭
Be my Savior; be my heart's delight.
Am F/A C/B♭ B♭M7 Gm7 F/A B♭2
Be my vision; be my guiding light.
Am7 Dm Gm F/A B♭2
Storms may press against me, threaten to prevail.
Am F/A C/B♭ B♭M7 Gm7 F/A
Be my refuge; be my shelter from the storm.
B♭2 Gm7 F/A B♭2
Be my love that keeps me warm; be my
Gm7 F/A B♭2 B♭ C F
Savior, be my light; be my home.

Text and music: Handt Hanson and Paul Murakami

Beauty for brokenness

God of the poor

17

G D/F♯ G7/F C/E
1 Beau - ty for bro - ken - ness, hope for de - spair:
2 Shel - ter for fra - gile lives, cures for their ills,
3 Ref - uge from cru - el wars, ha - vens from fear,
4 Rest for the rav - aged earth, o - ceans and streams,
5 Light - en our dark - ness, breathe on this flame,
Am7 D Bm7 Em7 Em/A D
Lord, in the suf - fer - ing this is our prayer.
work for the crafts - men, trade for their skills;
cit - ies for sanc - tu - a - ry, free - doms to share;
plun - dered and poi - soned, our fu - ture, our dreams.
un - til your jus - tice burns bright - ly a - gain;
B Em C G
Bread for the chil - dren, jus - tice, joy, peace;
land for the dis - pos - sessed, rights for the weak,
peace to the kill - ing fields, scorched earth to green,
Lord, end our mad - ness, care - less - ness, greed;
un - til the na - tions learn of your ways,
Bm7 C Am7 D G
sun - rise to sun - set your king - dom in - crease.
voic - es to plead the cause of those who can't speak.
Christ for the bit - ter - ness, his cross for the pain.
make us con - tent with the things that we need.
seek your sal - va - tion, and bring you their praise.
Refrain
D7 G B7 Em C Am7
God of the poor, friend of the weak, give us com - pas - sion, we
D D7/F♯ G B7 Em
pray; melt our cold hearts, let tears fall like rain.
C Am7 C/D G2
Come, change our love from a spark to a flame.

Text and music: Graham Kendrick

18 Bind us together

Refrain
F
Gm7
Am7
Dm7
Gm7
Bind us to - geth - er, Lord, bind us to - geth - er with cords that
C7 B♭/C C7
F
Gm7/C
F
Gm7
can - not be bro - ken. Bind us to - geth - er, Lord,
Am7
Dm7
Gm7
C7
F B♭/F F
bind us to - geth - er, Lord, bind us to - geth - er in love.
F
Gm7
Am7
Gm7
F
1 There is on - ly one God. There is
2 You are the fam - 'ly of God. You are the
Gm7
C7
F
B♭/F
F
Gm7
Am7
on - ly one King. There is on - ly one Bod - y;
prom - ise di - vine. You are God's cho - sen de - sire, . . .
Gm7
F
Gm7
C7
F
B♭/C
Refrain
that is why we can sing:
you are the glo - rious new wine.

Text and music: Bob Gillman

Bless his holy name

E♭ Edim7 B♭7/F B♭7 E♭ B♭7/F E♭7/G
Bless the Lord, O my soul: and all that is with -
A♭sus4/2 A♭ A♭m7 Cm7/G G♭dim B♭7/F B♭ E♭ A♭/E♭ E♭
in me, bless his ho - ly name.
Cm6 B♭7 Dm7(♭5) E♭
He has done great things, he has done great things,
E♭7 E♭/G A♭ Fm7(♭5) E♭/B♭ B♭7 E♭
he has done great things: bless his ho - ly name!
E♭ Edim7 B♭7/F B♭7 E♭ B♭7/F E♭7/G
Bless the Lord, O my soul: and all that is with -
A♭sus4/2 A♭ A♭m7 Cm7/G G♭dim B♭7/F B♭ E♭ A♭/E♭ E♭
in me, bless his ho - ly name.

Text and music: Andraé Crouch

Blessed be the Lord God of Israel

Refrain
Am7 G C F G CM7 E7(♭9)
Bless'd be the Lord God of Is - ra - el! Ho - ly is your name:
Am Gm7 C7 FM7 C/E Dm7 F/G C Gm7 C7
you have come to save your peo - ple from death and from the grave.
FM7 C
1 You have spo - ken through the proph - ets from age up - on
2 Lit - tle child, . . . you . . . shall be called the proph - et of the
Gm7 C7 FM7
age: the prom - ise giv - en to our an - ces - tors
Lord; the way of God . . . . you . . . . will pre - pare,
CM7 Gm7 C7 FM7
for - ev - er true will re - main. De - liv - 'ring us from our
bring - ing sal - va - tion through the Word. With ten - der mer - cy . . .
C Em7 A7(♭9)
en - em - ies, our God is al - ways near; in ho - li - ness and
from our God, the day - spring from on high brings us the light to
Refrain
Dm7 F/G CM7 E7(♭9)
righ - teous - ness we wor - ship with - out fear.
guide our feet and drive a - way the night.

Text: "Benedictus," Luke 1:68-79, adapt.
Music: Ralph C. Sappington

Blessing, honor, and glory

Bless - ing, hon - or, glo - ry to the Lamb.
Ho - ly, righ - teous, wor - thy is the Lamb.
Death could not hold him down, for he is ris - en!
Seat - ed up - on the throne, he is the Lamb of God!
God! Bless - ing, hon - or, glo - ry to the Lamb.
Ho - ly, righ - teous, wor - thy is the Lamb of God.

Text and music: Geoff Bullock and David Reidy

Bring forth the kingdom

Leader
D G/D D D/F♯
All
G D/F♯ A D
1 You are salt for the earth, O peo-ple: salt for the king-dom of God!
2 You are a light on the hill, O peo-ple: light for the cit-y of God!
3 You are a seed of the word, O peo-ple: bring forth the king-dom of God!
4 We are a blest and a pil-grim peo-ple: bound for the king-dom of God!
Leader
G D/F♯ G A D
All
G D/F♯ A D
Share the fla-vor of life, O peo-ple: life in the king-dom of God!
Shine so ho-ly and bright, O peo-ple: shine for the king-dom of God!
Seeds of mer-cy and seeds of jus-tice, grow in the king-dom of God!
Love our jour-ney and love our home-land: love is the king-dom of God!
Refrain
G D/F♯ Em A D G D/F♯
Bring forth the king-dom of mer-cy, bring forth the
Em A D G D/F♯ G A D
king-dom of peace; bring forth the king-dom of jus-tice,
G D/F♯ Em/G A D G D/F♯ A D
bring forth the cit-y of God!

Text and music: Marty Haugen

Broken for me

Refrain
E
AM7
F♯m7
B7sus B7
Bro - ken for me,
bro - ken for you;
E
AM7
F♯m7
B7
the bod - y of Je - sus bro - ken for you.
E
AM7
F♯m7
Bsus B
1 He of - fered his bod - y, he poured out his soul;
2 Come to my ta - ble and with me dine;
3 This is my bod - y giv - en for you;
4 This is my blood . . . I shed for you;
Refrain
E
AM7
F♯m7
B7sus B7
Je - sus was bro - ken that we might be whole.
eat of my bread . . . and drink of my wine.
eat it, re - mem - b'ring I died for you.
for your for - give - ness, mak - ing you new.
Final refrain
E
AM7
F♯m7
B7sus B7
Bro - ken for me, bro - ken for you;
E
AM7
F♯m7
A/B
E
the bod - y of Je - sus bro - ken for you.

Text: Janet Lunt
Music: Janet Lunt; arr. Mimi Farra

24 Broken in love

C F/C G/B F/A D/F♯
This is my bod - y, bro - ken in love; take it and
D G F/G C F/C
eat and re - mem - ber me. This is my blood,
G/B F/A D D/F♯ G
poured out in love; take it and drink and re - mem - ber
Am Am/G Am/F G/F FM7
me. For love is will - ing ev - 'ry day to
Em7 Dm7 G Am Am/G
die in or - der to live, and love is pa - tient
Am/F G/F FM7 Em7 Dm7 G
for a way to share the gifts that I give.
Last time
CM7

Text: Handt Hanson
Music: Handt Hanson; arr. Henry Wiens

By grace we have been saved

25

1 By grace we have been saved through faith and
2 For all have sinned and fall - en short. God's
3 God gave to earth a per - fect love through
4 We know the wage of sin is death; thank
5 Set free, we now have peace with God. Sal -
not by keep - ing law. God's saints be - lieved by
plan, not one o - beyed. Christ has for all ful -
Je - sus on the cross. While we were foes, Christ
God, we shall re - vive. For just as Je - sus
va - tion is se - cured. How beau - ti - ful the
what they heard and not by what they saw.
filled the law. Be - lieve, con - fess, be saved.
died for us. We gained by God's own loss.
rose a - gain, we too are made a - live.
feet of those who share this gos - pel word.
Refrain
Oh, how I love Je - sus! Oh, how I love Je - sus!
Oh, how I love Je - sus, be - cause he first loved me!

Text: Rusty Edwards, stanzas; Frederick Whitfield, refrain
Music: North American traditional, arr. Rusty Edwards

Canticle of the turning

Em C D
1 My soul cries out with a joy - ful shout that the
2 Though I am small, my . . . . God, my all, you . . .
3 From the halls of power to the for - tress tower, not a
4 Though the na - tions rage from . . . age to age, we re -
Em C D Em
God of my heart is great, and my spir - it sings of the
work great . . . things in me, and your mer - cy will last from the
stone will be left on stone. Let the king be - ware for your
mem - ber who holds us fast: God's . . . mer - cy must de -
G D Em C Em
won - drous things that you bring to the ones who wait. You
depths of the past to the end of the age to be. Your
jus - tice tears ev - 'ry ty - rant . . . from his throne. The
liv - er us from the con - quer - or's crush - ing grasp. This
G D
fixed your sight on your ser - vant's plight, and my
ver - y name puts the proud to shame, and to
hun - gry poor shall . . . weep no more, for the
sav - ing word that our fore - bears heard is the
Em C D Em
weak - ness you did not spurn, so from east to west shall my
those who would for you yearn, you will show your might, put the
food they can nev - er earn; there are ta - bles spread, ev - 'ry
prom - ise which holds us bound, 'til the spear and rod can be
G D Em C Em
name be blest. Could the world be a - bout to turn?
strong to flight, for the world is a - bout to turn.
mouth be fed, for the world is a - bout to turn.
crushed by God, who is turn - ing the world a - round.

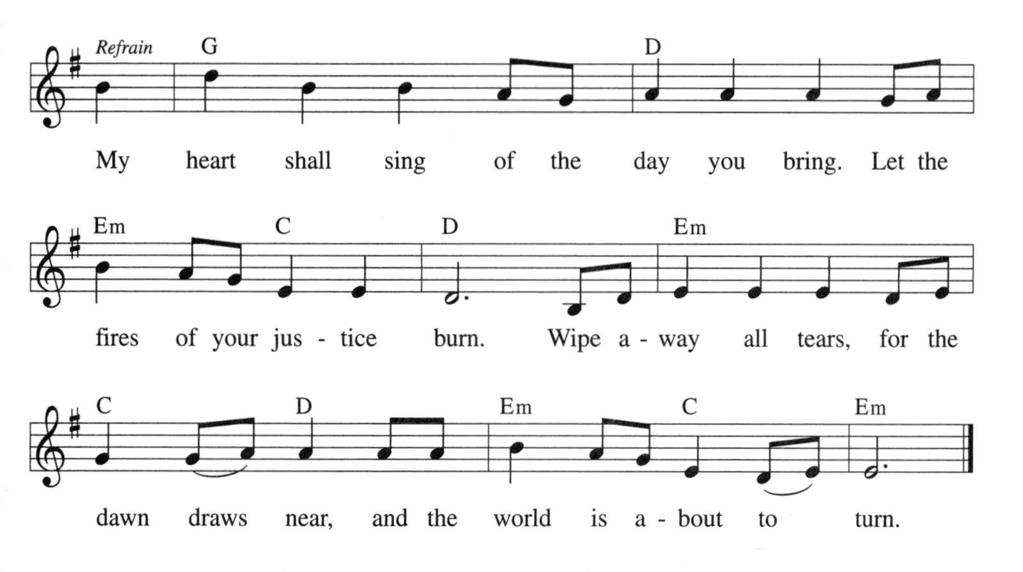
Refrain
G D
My heart shall sing of the day you bring. Let the
Em C D Em
fires of your jus - tice burn. Wipe a - way all tears, for the
C D Em C Em
dawn draws near, and the world is a - bout to turn.

Text: Rory Cooney, based on the Magnificat, Luke 1:46-55
Music: Irish traditional, adapt. Rory Cooney

Cares chorus

27

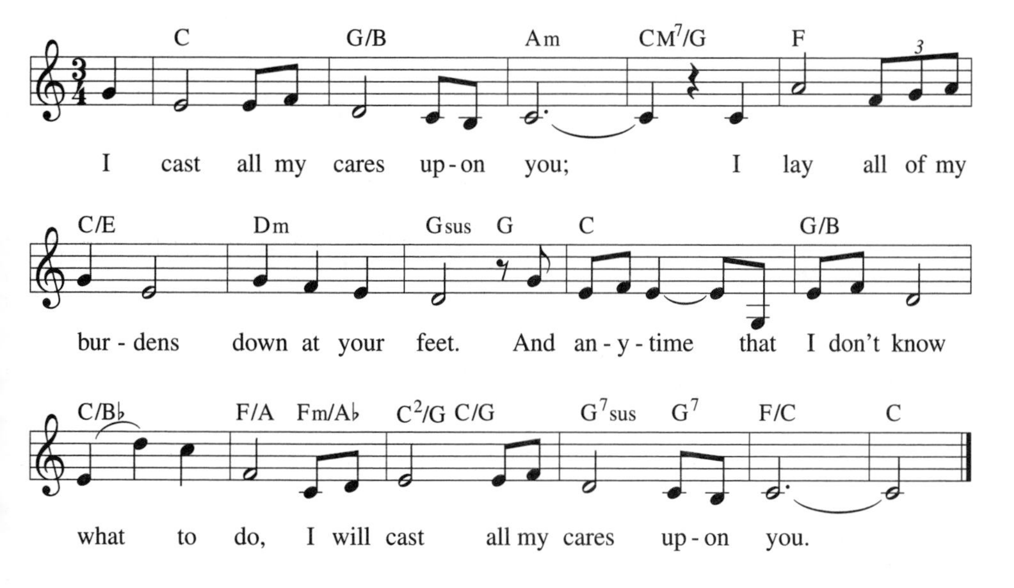
C G/B Am CM7/G F
I cast all my cares up - on you; I lay all of my
C/E Dm Gsus G C G/B
bur - dens down at your feet. And an - y - time that I don't know
C/B♭ F/A Fm/A♭ C2/G C/G G7sus G7 F/C C
what to do, I will cast all my cares up - on you.

Text and music: Kelly Willard

Change my heart, O God

C Em7 Dm7 G7sus G7 C Dm/C
Change my heart, O God. Make it ev - er true.
C2 Am7 Dm7 G7sus G7 C
Change my heart, O God. May I be like you.
E7 Bm7 E7 Am7 Dm7 G7 C
You are the pot - ter, I am the clay;
E7 Bm7 E7 Am7 C/D D7 G7sus G7
mold me and make me, this is what I pray.
C2 Em7 Dm7 G7sus G7 C Dm/C
Change my heart, O God. Make it ev - er true.
C2 Am7 Dm7 G7sus G7 C
Change my heart, O God. May I be like you.

Text and music: Eddie Espinosa

Come and see

1 Come and see the glo - ry of the Lord. Come, be-hold the
2 Come and give thanks un - to the Lord. Come, be-hold the
Lamb. Come and see the mer - cy of the King,
Lamb. Come and sing the prais - es of the King,
bow-ing down be - fore him.
bow-ing down be - fore him. For he is
Lord a - bove the heav - ens, Lord in all the earth,
Lord of all the an - gels, wor - thy to be served.
Al - le - lu - ia. Al - le - lu - ia, Lord.

Text and music: Lenny LeBlanc

Come and taste

F C/E B♭/D
Come and taste and see how good the love of God can be!
C/E Gm D7/F♯
Come and taste and see how good the love of God
Gm/F C B♭/C C B♭M7 Am7
can be! We come here bro-ken - heart - ed,
Gm7 B♭m6/C F
seek - ing all that God of - fers. Come and taste and
C/E B♭/D C/E F
see how good the love of God can be! Come see!

Text: Handt Hanson and Paul Murakami
Music: Handt Hanson and Paul Murakami; arr. Henry Wiens

Come, let us worship and bow down

D G2 G/B D/A A7/G D/F♯
Come, let us wor - ship and bow down; let us
G Em7 G/B A
kneel be - fore the Lord, our God, our mak - er.
D G2 G/B D/A A7/G D/F♯
Come, let us wor - ship and bow down; let us
G Em7 G/B A
kneel be - fore the Lord, our God, our mak - er. For
G D/F♯ Em7 D/F♯ G D/F♯ G
he is our God, and we are the peo - ple of his
G/A G A
pas - ture, and the sheep of his
D Bm7 D/A G A D
hand, and the sheep of his hand.

Text: Psalm 95:6-7
Music: Dave Doherty

32 Come to the mountain

Eb
1 Je - sus took Pet - er, James, and John
2 "This is my Son!" said a voice from the cloud.
3 We will be changed like Je - sus our Lord,
Eb/Bb Bb
up to the moun - tain to be a - lone.
"Lis - ten to him . . . . . . and do what he says!"
and live with him . . . . . . in heav - en a - bove.
Eb G7 Cm
While they were watch - ing Je - sus was changed;
Soon as it came . . . . . . that vis - ion was gone,
But while we live on this earth - ly home,
Ab Eb/Bb Ab Eb
and they saw Mo - ses face to face.
and they saw Je - sus stand - ing a - lone.
our work as ser - vants nev - er is done.
Refrain
Ab Eb Eb/Bb Eb
Come to the moun - tain to see the light.
Ab Eb F7 Bb
Come to the moun - tain to hear God's word.
Ab Eb G7 Cm
Go to the val - ley, it is your home.
Ab Eb/Bb Ab/Bb Bb7 Eb
Go to the val - ley to serve the Lord.

Text: Scott Tunseth
Music: Kathy Donlan Tunseth

Come to the table

F
Bb/F
C/E
Dsus4/2
Dm7/C
Bb
C7sus
Come to the table of mercy, prepared with the wine and the
F
Gm7
Bb/C
F
Bb/F
Dsus4/2
Dm7/C
bread. All who are hungry and thirsty,
Bb
C7sus
Fsus
F
Am
BbM7
come and your souls will be fed. Come at the Lord's invi-
C7/Bb
Am
Dm7
Gm7
Dm/F
C/E
Bb/D
C
ta-tion; re-ceive from his nail-scarred hand.
F
Bb/F
C/E
Dsus4/2
Dm7/C
Bb
C7sus
Fsus F
Eat of the bread of sal-va-tion; drink of the blood of the Lamb.

Text: Claire Cloninger
Music: Martin J. Nystrom

Create in me a clean heart

G D C G C/D
Cre - ate in me a clean heart, O God,
G D Dsus D G C/D
and re - new a right spir - it with - in me.
G D C G C/D
Cre - ate in me a clean heart, O God,
G D Dsus D G C/D
and re - new a right spir - it with - in me.
G7 C G/C D G Gsus
Cast me not a - way from your pres - ence, O
G C G/C D G
Lord, and take not your Ho - ly Spir - it from me.
G7 C G/C D G D/F♯ Em
Re - store un - to me the joy of your sal - va - tion,
C D Dsus D G
and re - new a right spir - it with - in me.

Text: Psalm 51:10-12
Music: anonymous

Create in me a clean heart

F C/E C/D Dm Dm/C B♭ Gm
Cre - ate in me a clean heart, O God, that I might serve
C7sus C7 F C/E C/D Dm Dm/C
you; cre - ate in me a clean heart, O God, that
Gm F/A C F Am7 Dm7
I might be re - newed. So fill me and
Am7 Dm7 Gm7 Gm/D C7sus C7
heal me, and bring me back to you. Cre -
F C/E C/D Dm Dm/C Gm F/A C F
ate in me a clean heart, O God, that I might serve you.

Text and music: Mary Rice Hopkins

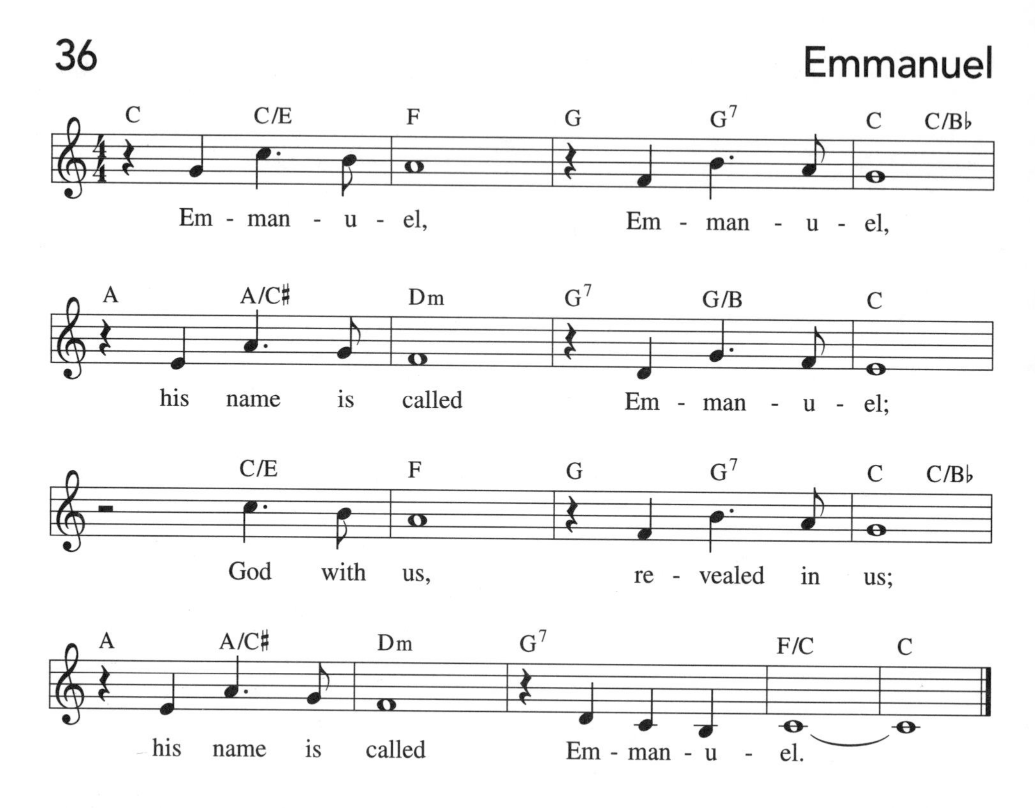
36
Emmanuel
C C/E F G G7 C C/B♭
Em - man - u - el, Em - man - u - el,
A A/C♯ Dm G7 G/B C
his name is called Em - man - u - el;
C/E F G G7 C C/B♭
God with us, re - vealed in us;
A A/C♯ Dm G7 F/C C
his name is called Em - man - u - el.

Text and music: Bob McGee

37

Father, I adore you

1* F Gm C F 2 Gm

1 Fa - ther,
2 Je - sus, I a - dore you, lay my life be -
3 Spir - it,

C F 3 Gm C F

fore you; how I love you.

may be sung in canon

Text and music: Terry Coelho

For by grace

E2
For by grace you have been saved through faith, and this is
A2 E2
not your own do - ing; it is the gift of God.
A C
Sal - va - tion, sal - va - tion,
G F
sal - va - tion, sal - va - tion:
Guitar tacet
E2
it is the gift of God.
E2
For by grace you have been saved through faith, and this is
A2 E2
not your own do - ing; it is the gift of God.

Text: Ephesians 2:8
Music: Thomas Ian Nicholas

39 For God so loved

Em D
For God so loved the world that he gave his
C Bm7 Em
on - ly be - got - ten Son, that who - so - ev - er be -
D C Bm7 Em D7
lieves in him should not per - ish, but
G D7 Em
have life ev - er - last - ing, have life ev - er -
D G D7
last - ing, have life ev - er - last - ing,
Em B7 Em
have life ev - er - last - ing. For God so loved the world that he
D C Bm7 Em
gave his on - ly be - got - ten Son.

Text: John 3:16, adapt. Stuart Dauermann
Music: Stuart Dauermann

From where the sun rises

D G A D Bm
1 From where the sun ris - es, e - ven to the place it goes down,
2 We're lift - ing our fac - es, look - ing at the one we all love:
Em A7 D
we're giv - ing you praise, giv - ing you praise.
we're giv - ing you praise, giv - ing you praise.
G A D
From sun - kissed is - lands, and e - ven where the cold wind blows,
All col - ors and rac - es, join - ing with the an - gels a - bove,
Bm Em A7 D
Fine
we're giv - ing you praise, giv - ing you praise.
we're giv - ing you praise, giv - ing you praise.
A
E - ven in the night when the sun goes down, we're
D A
giv - ing you praise; pass - ing it a - long as the
G D A
D.C. (stanza 2) al fine
world goes 'round, we're giv-ing you praise.

Text and music: Graham Kendrick

41 Give thanks

Give thanks with a grate-ful heart, give thanks to the Ho-ly One,
give thanks be-cause he's giv-en Je-sus Christ, his Son.
Give thanks with a grate-ful heart, give thanks to the Ho-ly One,
give thanks be-cause he's giv-en Je-sus Christ, his Son.
And now let the weak say, "I am strong," let the poor say, "I am
rich," be-cause of what the Lord has done for us. And
now let the weak say, "I am strong," let the poor say, "I am
rich," be-cause of what the Lord has done for us.
Last time
Give thanks!

Text and music: Henry Smith

Glorify thy name

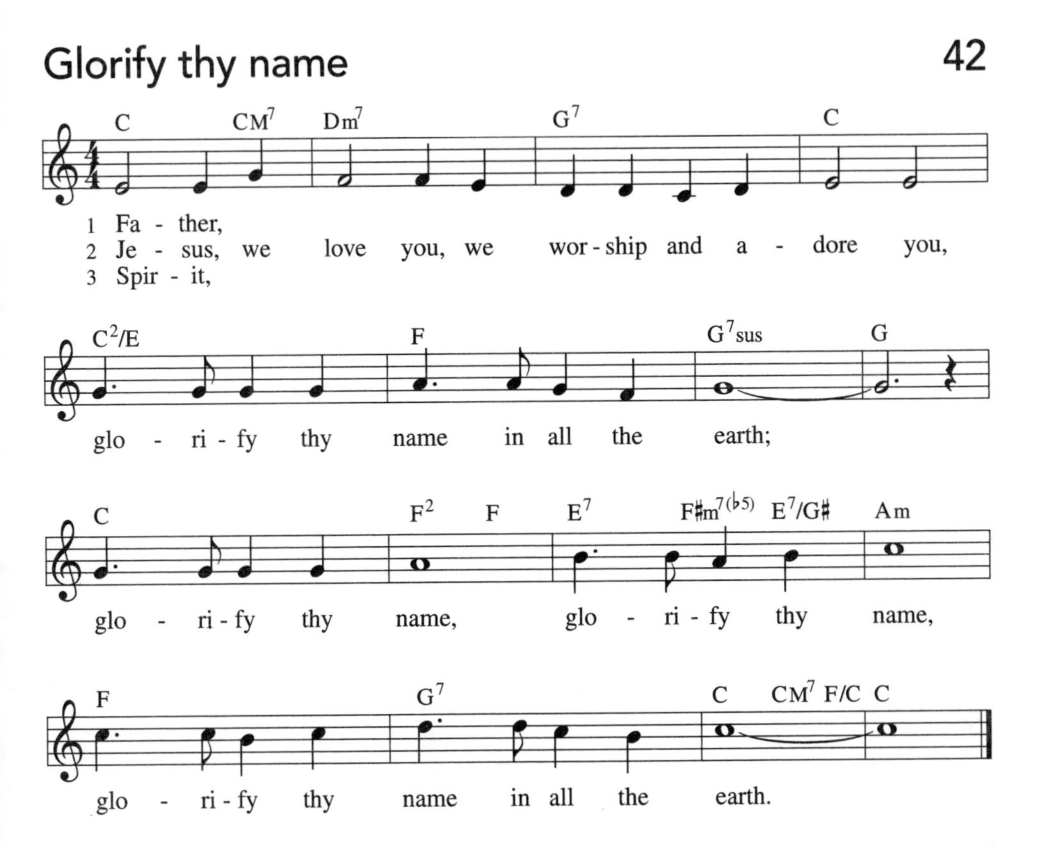
C CM7 Dm7 G7 C
1 Fa - ther,
2 Je - sus, we love you, we wor - ship and a - dore you,
3 Spir - it,
C2/E F G7sus G
glo - ri - fy thy name in all the earth;
C F2 F E7 F♯m7(♭5) E7/G♯ Am
glo - ri - fy thy name, glo - ri - fy thy name,
F G7 C CM7 F/C C
glo - ri - fy thy name in all the earth.

Text and music: Donna Adkins

43

Glory and praise to our God

Refrain
G D Em G
Glo - ry and praise to our God, who a - lone gives
Dsus D Am/C Am
light to our days. Man - y are the
G Bm C D G 4th time to stanza 4
bless - ings he bears to those who trust in his ways.
Dm7 C Am D
1 We, the daugh - ters and sons of him who built the
2 In his wis - dom he strength - ens us, like gold that's
3 Ev - 'ry mo - ment of ev - 'ry day our God is
G Dm7 C
val - leys and plains, praise the won - ders our God has
test - ed in fire. Though the pow - er of sin pre -
wait - ing to save, al - ways read - y to seek the
Bm7 Em A D D9/C G/B D/A Refrain
done in ev - 'ry heart that sings.
vails, our God is there to save.
lost, to an - swer those who pray.

B7
Em
B7
4 God has wa - tered our bar - ren land and spent his
Em
C
G
mer - ci - ful rain. Now the riv - ers of life run
Em
Am
D
D9/C
G/B
D/A
full for an - y - one to drink.
Final refrain
G
D
Em
G
Glo - ry and praise to our God, who a - lone gives
Dsus
D
Am/C
Am
light to our days. Man - y are the
G
Bm
C
D
G
bless - ings he bears to those who trust in his ways.

Text and music: Daniel Schutte

Glory to God

Refrain
F
E♭/F
B♭/F
C/F
Glo-ry, glo-ry to God, glo-ry in the high-est;
Dm
Am
B♭
B♭/C
3rd time to stanza 3
peace, peace to God's peo-ple on earth.
(3) For
1 Lord God, heav-en-ly king, al-might-y
God and Fa-ther, we wor-ship you, we
Gm
F/A
C
give you thanks, we praise you for your glo-ry.
2 Lord Je-sus Christ, on-ly Son of the
Fa-ther, Lord God, Lamb of God,

Gm7 F/A B♭ B♭/C C E♭
you take a - way the sin of the world: have mer -
B♭/D B♭/C C D♭ E♭/D♭ D♭
cy on us; you are seat - ed at the right hand
E♭/D♭ B♭/C C B♭/C C Refrain
of the Fa - ther: re - ceive our prayer.
Dm Am B♭ C Dm Am
3 For you a - lone are the Ho - ly One, you a - lone are the
B♭ C Dm Am B♭ C E♭ B♭/D
Lord, you a - lone are the Most High, Je - sus
B♭/C C D♭ E♭/D♭ D♭
Christ, with the Ho - ly Spir - it, in the glo - ry of
E♭/D♭ B♭/C C Refrain
God the Fa - ther. A - men

Text: "Gloria," tr. English Language Liturgical Consultation
Music: David Haas

45
Glory to God
We praise you for your glory
1 Glo-ry to God in the high - est, peace to his peo - ple on earth;
2 Je - sus, our Lord . . . and Sav - ior, rul - ing in glo - ry a - bove,
al - might - y God, the Fa - ther, the heav - en - ly
au - thor of life and cre - a - tor of in - fi - nite
king.
love:
Glo - ry to God in the high -
We call on you now for mer -
- est, peace to his peo - ple on earth;
- cy, we pray for your heal - ing with - in;
al-might - y God, the Fa - ther, the heav-en - ly king.
O Lamb of God, so wor - thy, for-give us our sin.

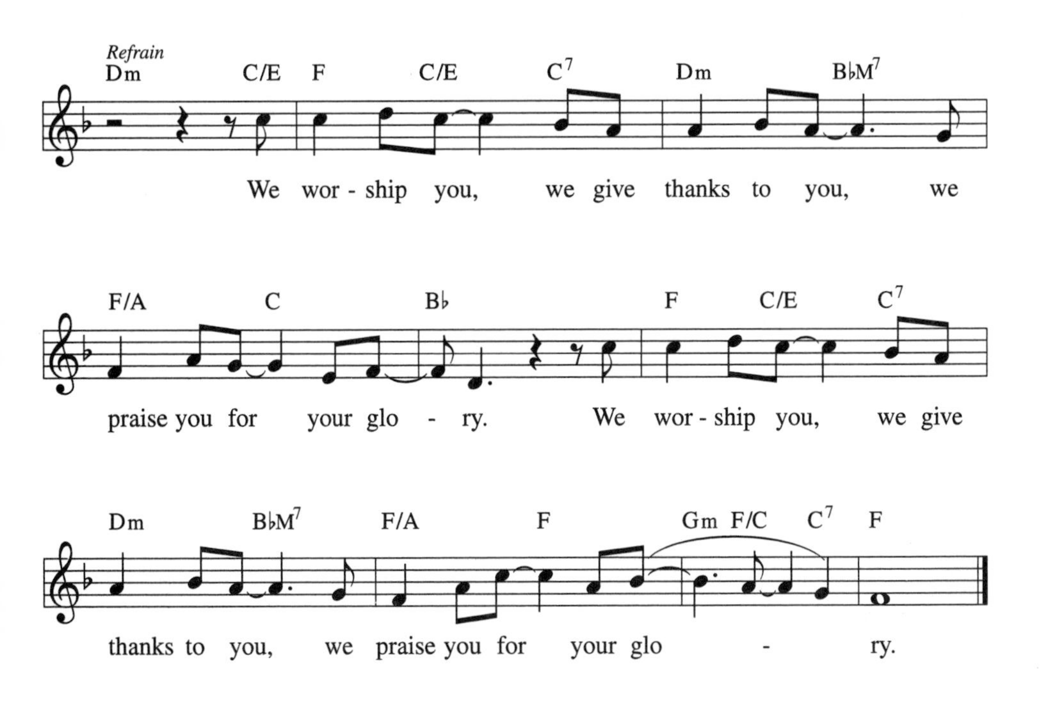
Refrain
Dm C/E F C/E C7 Dm B♭M7
We wor - ship you, we give thanks to you, we
F/A C B♭ F C/E C7
praise you for your glo - ry. We wor - ship you, we give
Dm B♭M7 F/A F Gm F/C C7 F
thanks to you, we praise you for your glo - ry.

Text: "Gloria," adapt. Rick Founds and Bill Batstone
Music: Rick Founds and Bill Batstone

You alone are the Holy

You alone are the Holy;
you alone are the Lord;
you alone are the Most High, the Most High God:
Jesus, our Lord and Messiah,
Spirit of power and love,
one with the Father in glory forever. Amen

This stanza completes the traditional "Glory to God" hymn text begun on the previous page.

Text: "Gloria," adapt. *Worship & Praise*

Go in peace and serve the Lord

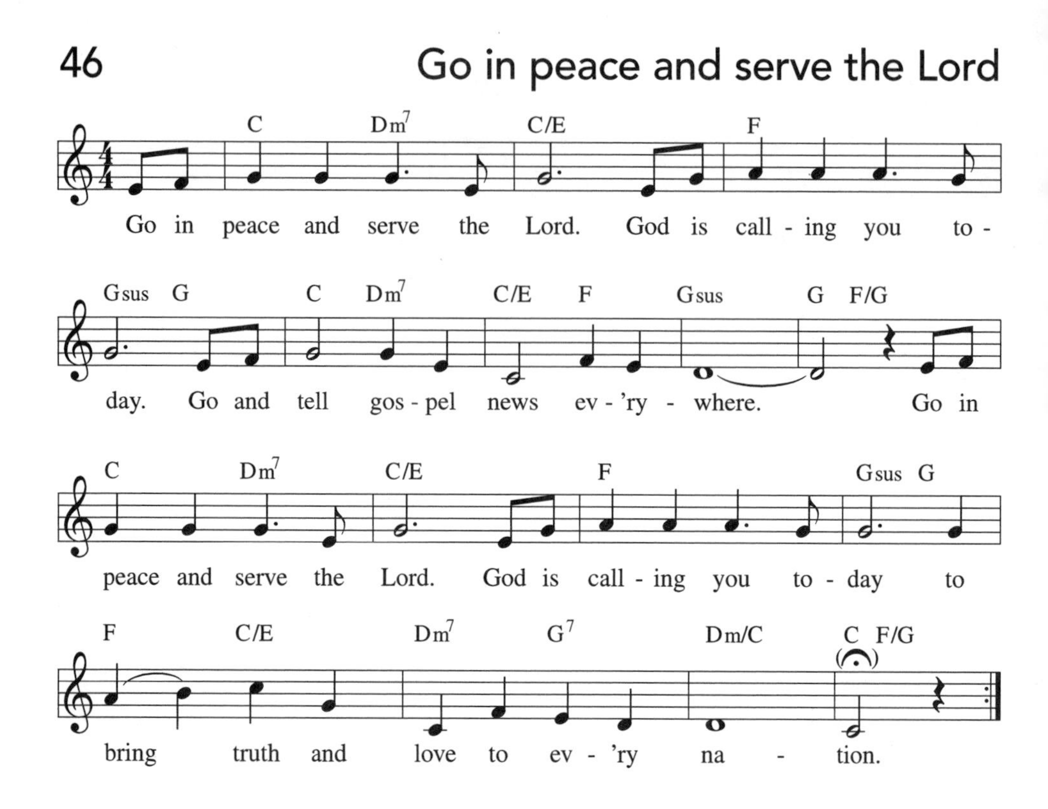
C Dm7 C/E F
Go in peace and serve the Lord. God is call - ing you to -
Gsus G C Dm7 C/E F Gsus G F/G
day. Go and tell gos - pel news ev - 'ry - where. Go in
C Dm7 C/E F Gsus G
peace and serve the Lord. God is call - ing you to - day to
F C/E Dm7 G7 Dm/C C F/G
bring truth and love to ev - 'ry na - tion.

Text: Handt Hanson
Music: Handt Hanson; arr. Henry Wiens

Go, make disciples
47
F C/E F Gm7 F/A C
Go, make dis - ci - ples, bap - tiz - ing them,
Dm C B♭ Csus F C/E F
teach - ing them. Go, make dis - ci - ples, for
Gm7 Fsus2/A B♭ F/B♭ Csus B♭/C B♭M7
I am with you till the end of time. Go, be the
Am7 Gm7 B♭/C FM7 C/E
salt of the earth. Go, be the light for the world.
Dm Am7 B♭M7 C/B♭
Go, be a cit - y on a hill, so all can see that you're
B♭/C F/C C B♭/C F C/E F
serv - ing me. Go, make dis - ci - ples.

Text: Handt Hanson
Music: Handt Hanson; arr. Henry Wiens

Go out with joy

Em
Am
CM7
Go out with joy and be led forth in peace, the moun - tains and the hills
Bm7
Em
shall break forth sing - ing. Go out with joy and be
Am
CM7
led forth in peace, the moun - tains and the hills shall break forth
Em
Am7
D7
GM7
Em
sing - ing. And all the trees of the field shall clap their hands, the
Am
D
Em B7/F♯ Em/G Em
Am7
D7
Lord al - might-y shall be praised. And all the trees of the field
GM7
CM7
Am
Bm7
Em
shall clap their hands, the word of the Lord shall be for - ev - er.

Text and music: Leila Huerta and Joe Huerta

Go ye therefore

D
Bm7
Go ye there - fore and make dis - ci - ples of
Em7
D/F♯
G
D/A
A
all na - tions, of all na - tions.
D
Bm7
Go ye there - fore and make dis - ci - ples of
Em7
D/F♯
G
D/A
A
all na - tions, of all na - tions,
GM9
D/F♯
bap - tiz - ing them in the name of the Fa - ther and the
Em7
Asus
A7
Son and the Ho - ly Spir - it.
D
Bm7
Go ye there - fore and make dis - ci - ples of
Em7(add4)
D/F♯
G
D/A
A
D
all na - tions, of all na - tions. Go!

Text: Matthew 28:19
Music: Robin Cain; arr. Richard Webb

50 God be with you

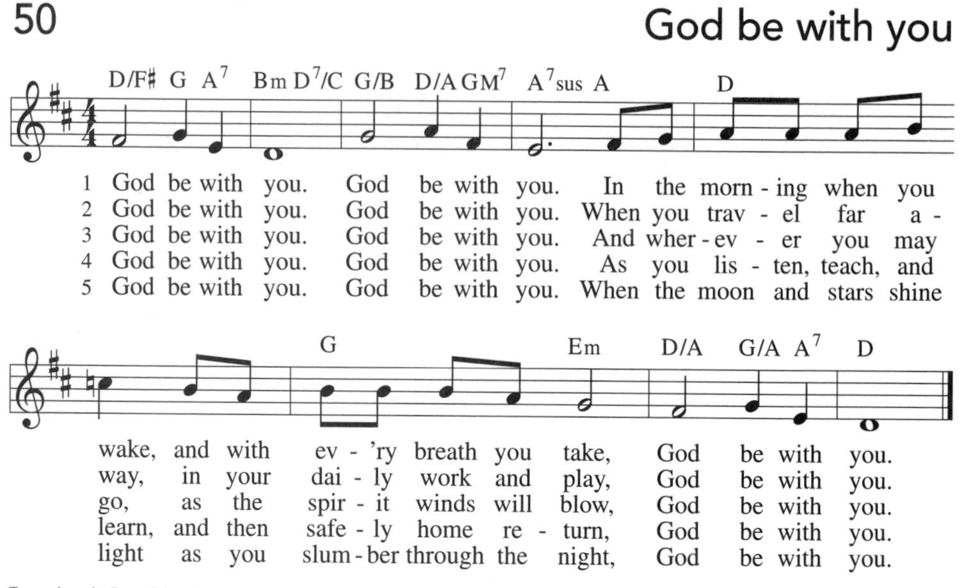
D/F♯ G A7 Bm D7/C G/B D/A GM7 A7sus A D
1 God be with you. God be with you. In the morn - ing when you
2 God be with you. God be with you. When you trav - el far a -
3 God be with you. God be with you. And wher - ev - er you may
4 God be with you. God be with you. As you lis - ten, teach, and
5 God be with you. God be with you. When the moon and stars shine
G Em D/A G/A A7 D
wake, and with ev - 'ry breath you take, God be with you.
way, in your dai - ly work and play, God be with you.
go, as the spir - it winds will blow, God be with you.
learn, and then safe - ly home re - turn, God be with you.
light as you slum - ber through the night, God be with you.

Text and music: Rusty Edwards

51 God has done marvelous things

Earth and all stars!

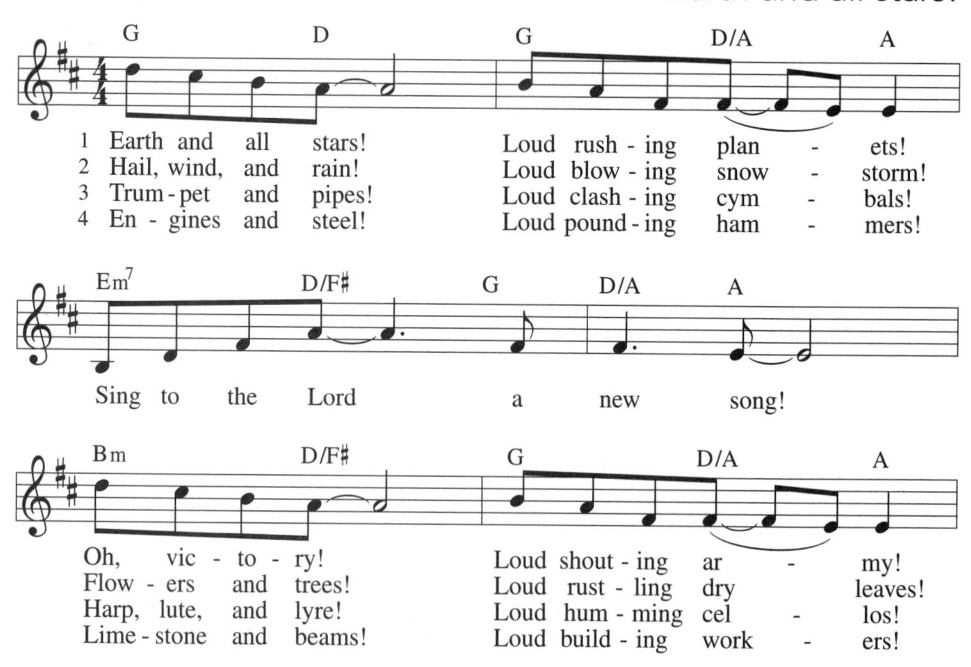
G D G D/A A
1 Earth and all stars! Loud rush - ing plan - ets!
2 Hail, wind, and rain! Loud blow - ing snow - storm!
3 Trum - pet and pipes! Loud clash - ing cym - bals!
4 En - gines and steel! Loud pound - ing ham - mers!
Em7 D/F♯ G D/A A
Sing to the Lord a new song!
Bm D/F♯ G D/A A
Oh, vic - to - ry! Loud shout - ing ar - my!
Flow - ers and trees! Loud rust - ling dry leaves!
Harp, lute, and lyre! Loud hum - ming cel - los!
Lime - stone and beams! Loud build - ing work - ers!

Em7 D/F♯ G G/A D
Sing to the Lord a new song!
Refrain
A/C♯ A D/F♯ G/B D/A G
God has done mar - vel - ous things. I too, I
Em7 D/F♯ G D/A A
too sing prais - es with a new song!
A/C♯ A D/F♯ G/B D/A G
God has done mar - vel - ous things. I too, I
Em7 D/F♯ G
To stanzas
G/A D G/D D D/A A
too sing prais - es with a new song!
Last time
G/A Bm Em7 D/F♯ G G/A A G D D/A A D
new song! I too sing prais - es with a new song!

5 Classroms and labs!
Loud boiling test tubes!
Sing to the Lord a new song!
Athlete and band!
Loud cheering people!
Sing to the Lord a new song!
Refrain

6 Knowledge and truth!
Loud sounding wisdom!
Sing to the Lord a new song!
Daughter and son!
Loud praying members!
Sing to the Lord a new song!
Refrain

Text: Herbert Brokering
Music: David Haas

Good soil

E G♯m7 A E/G♯ F♯m7 B
Lord, let my heart be good soil, o-pen to the seed of your
EM7 B7sus E G♯m7 A E/G♯
word. Lord, let my heart be good soil, where
F♯m7 A/B B7 E A E/G♯
love can grow and peace is un-der-stood. When my heart is hard,
F♯m7 A/B B A E/G♯ F♯m7 A/B B
break the stone a-way. When my heart is cold, warm it with the day.
G♯(♭9)/B♯ C♯m A F♯m7(♭5)/C E/B A/B
When my heart is lost, lead me on your way. Lord, let my heart,
E A/B E/G♯ A/B F♯m/E E
Lord, let my heart, Lord, let my heart be good soil.

Text: Handt Hanson
Music: Handt Hanson; arr. Henry Wiens

Great is the Lord

C Dm G/B C
Great is the Lord, he is ho - ly and just, by his
F/A G F C/E Dm7 C C Dm
pow - er we trust in his love. Great is the Lord, he is
G/B C F/A G
faith - ful and true, by his mer - cy he proves he is
F C/E Dm7 C B♭/C F/C B♭/C F C/E Dm7 C
love. Great is the Lord, and wor - thy of glo - ry.
B♭/C F/C B♭/C G/C C B♭/C F/C B♭/C
Great is the Lord, and wor - thy of praise. Great is the Lord, now
D G E Am Dm Gsus G
lift up your voice, now lift up your voice: Great is the
Am Am7/G Dm Gsus G C Csus C
Lord! Great is the Lord!

Text and music: Michael W. Smith and Deborah D. Smith

54
He has made me glad
D G D/A A Bm
I will en - ter his gates with thanks - giv - ing in my heart,
D G A
I will en - ter his courts with praise.
D G D F♯ Bm
I will say this is the day that the Lord has made;
Em7 A7 D A7
I will re - joice for he has made me glad.
D G D Bm
He has made me glad, he has made me glad,
Em7 A7 D
I will re - joice for he has made me glad.
G G♯dim7 D/A A Bm
He has made me glad, he has made me glad,
Em7 A D
I will re - joice for he has made me glad.

Text: Psalm 100:4 and 118:24, adapt. Leona von Brethorst
Music: Leona von Brethorst

He is exalted

F F/A B♭ B♭/D C/E
He is ex-alt-ed, the King is ex-alt-ed on high; I will praise him.
F F/A B♭ C/B♭ B♭/C C
He is ex-alt-ed, for-ev-er ex-alt-ed, and I will praise his
Dsus D/C Gm Dm/F C/E C F Am
name. Je-sus is Lord, for-ev-er his truth shall
B♭ F/A Gm Dm/F C/E C F Am
reign; hea-ven and earth re-joice in his ho-ly
B♭ F/A Gm B♭/F E♭M7 B♭/C F B♭/F F
name. He is ex-alt-ed, the King is ex-alt-ed on high.

Text and music: Twila Paris

56 He who began a good work in you

G Bm7 C D D/C Bm7 Em7
He who be - gan a good work in you,
Am D7 G Bm7 C D D/C Bm7
he who be - gan a good work in you
E7 Am7
will be faith - ful to com - plete it,
D7 Am7 D7
will be faith - ful to com - plete it. He who start -
Am7 G/B C C/D D7 G
- ed the work will be faith - ful to com - plete it in you.

Text and music: Jon Mohr

Hear the angels

Em D/E C/E D/E
1, 4 Hear the an - gels sing; Christ is com - ing!
2 Hear the shep - herds sing; come and fol - low
3 Hear the wise men sing; come and wor - ship
Em D/E Am7 B7sus B7
Hear them tell of the Sav - ior's birth.
by the light of the morn - ing star.
Christ the child, who was born to be king.
Em Bm/D C GM7/B
Hear the an - gels sing; Christ is com - ing!
Hear the shep - herds sing, "Come and fol - low; to
Hear the wise men sing, "Come and wor - ship.
Am9 G9 F♯m7 Bm7 Em D/E
"Glo - ry to God, and peace to the earth."
wor - ship the child we will trav - el a - far."
Gold, spice, and myrrh are the gifts that we bring."
Refrain
Em D/F♯ G D Am D
An - gels sing!
Al - le - lu - ia! Shep - herds sing! Al - le -
Wise men sing!
G D Am7 D/F♯ C/E D/F♯ G D
lu - ia! A Sav - ior is born, al - le - lu - ia!
Am7 D G D Am B7sus
Christ is com - ing. All of heav - en and earth, a - dore.

Text: Robin Cain
Music: Robin Cain and Phil Kadidlo

57

Here is bread

G/B Am E7 F/A C/G G
1 Here is bread, here is wine, Christ is with us,
2 Here is grace, here is peace, Christ is with us,
3 Here we are, joined in one, Christ is with us,
F/A Am G/B C G/B Am E7
he is with us. Break the bread, taste the wine,
he is with us. Know his grace, find his peace,
he is with us. We'll pro - claim till he comes
F/A C/G G 1 C Fm/C 2, 3 C Gm7 B♭/C
Christ is with us here.
feast on Je - sus here.
Je - sus cru - ci - fied.
Refrain
FM7 F6 Em7 Am7 Dm7 Gm7
In this bread there is heal - ing, in this cup is
B♭/C C B♭/D C/E FM7 F♯dim7
life for - ev - er. In this mo - ment,
Em7 A7aug Dm7 G7 C
by the Spir - it, Christ is with us here.

Text and music: Graham Kendrick

Holy ground

A♭/B♭ E♭ B♭7/F E♭/G A♭ E♭/G B♭7/A♭ E♭/G
We are stand - ing on ho - ly ground,
A♭/B♭ A♭M7 Gm7(♭5) C C/B♭ F9/A A♭m6
and I know that there are an - gels all a - round.
E♭/G B♭7/F E♭/G A♭ E♭/G B♭7/A♭ E♭/G
Let us praise Je - sus now.
A♭ E♭/G A♭ E♭/B♭ B♭7 E♭sus E♭
We are stand - ing in his pres - ence on ho - ly ground.

Text and music: Geron Davis

60 Holy, holy

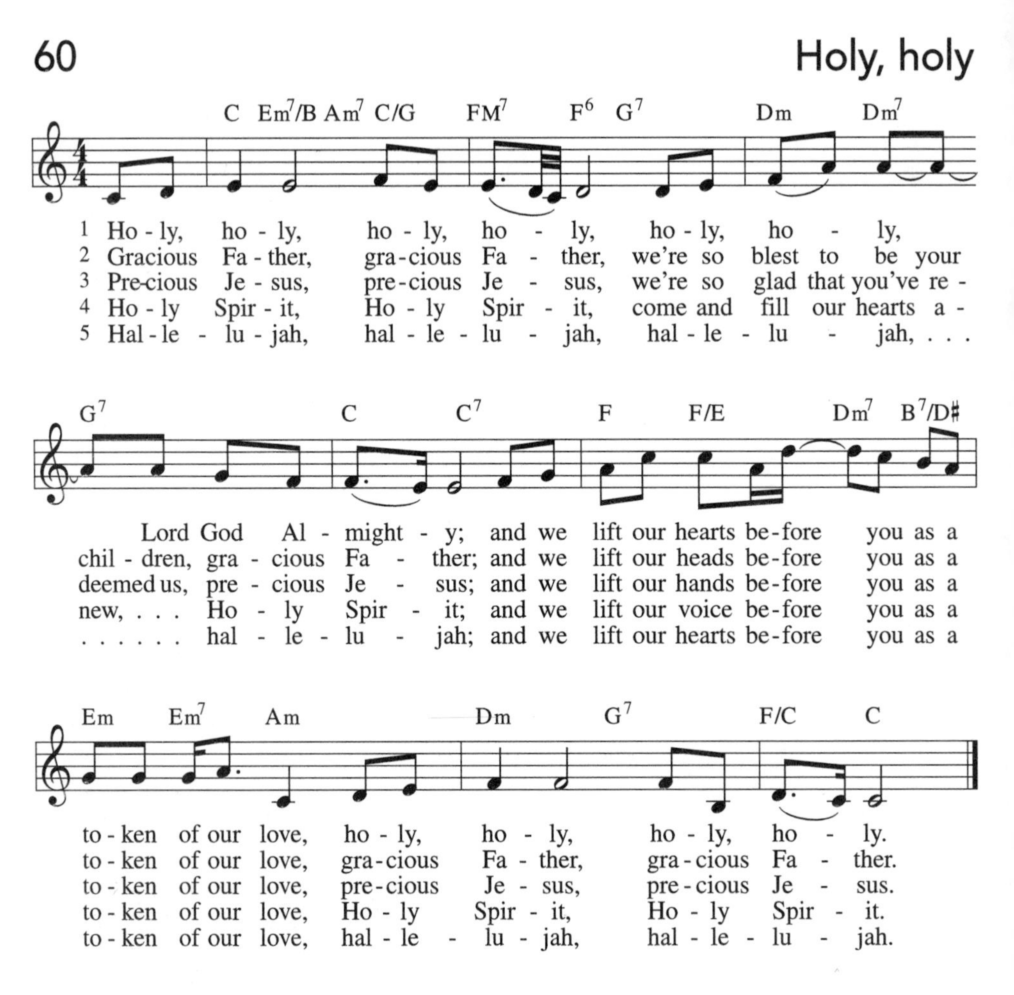
C Em7/B Am7 C/G FM7 F6 G7 Dm Dm7
1 Ho - ly, ho - ly, ho - ly, ho - ly, ho - ly, ho - ly,
2 Gracious Fa - ther, gra - cious Fa - ther, we're so blest to be your
3 Pre-cious Je - sus, pre - cious Je - sus, we're so glad that you've re -
4 Ho - ly Spir - it, Ho - ly Spir - it, come and fill our hearts a -
5 Hal - le - lu - jah, hal - le - lu - jah, hal - le - lu - jah, . . .
G7 C C7 F F/E Dm7 B7/D♯
Lord God Al - might - y; and we lift our hearts be - fore you as a
chil - dren, gra - cious Fa - ther; and we lift our heads be - fore you as a
deemed us, pre - cious Je - sus; and we lift our hands be - fore you as a
new, . . . Ho - ly Spir - it; and we lift our voice be - fore you as a
. . . . . . hal - le - lu - jah; and we lift our hearts be - fore you as a
Em Em7 Am Dm G7 F/C C
to - ken of our love, ho - ly, ho - ly, ho - ly, ho - ly.
to - ken of our love, gra - cious Fa - ther, gra - cious Fa - ther.
to - ken of our love, pre - cious Je - sus, pre - cious Je - sus.
to - ken of our love, Ho - ly Spir - it, Ho - ly Spir - it.
to - ken of our love, hal - le - lu - jah, hal - le - lu - jah.

Text and music: Jimmy Owens

61 Holy, holy, holy
Santo, santo, santo

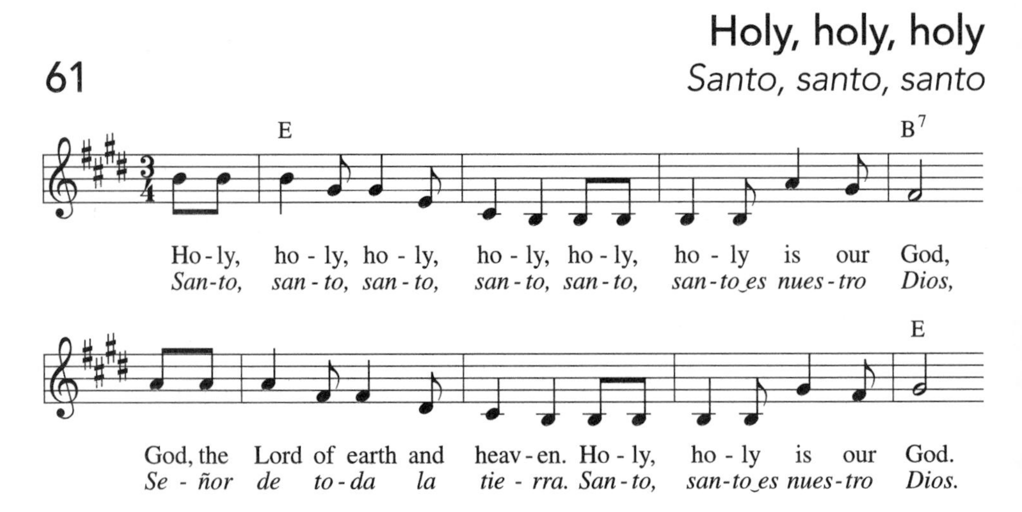
E B7
Ho - ly, ho - ly, ho - ly, ho - ly, ho - ly, ho - ly is our God,
San-to, san - to, san - to, san - to, san - to, san - to es nues - tro Dios,
E
God, the Lord of earth and heav - en. Ho - ly, ho - ly is our God.
Se - ñor de to - da la tie - rra. San - to, san - to es nues - tro Dios.

B7
Ho - ly, ho - ly, ho - ly, ho - ly, ho - ly, ho - ly is our God,
San-to, san - to, san - to, san - to, san - to, san-to‿es nues - tro Dios,
E Fine
God, the Lord of all of his-t'ry. Ho - ly, ho - ly is our God.
Se - ñor de to-da la‿his - to - ria. San - to, san-to‿es nues-tro Dios.
E A
Who ac - com - pa - nies our peo - ple, who
Que‿a - com - pa - ña‿a nues - tro pue - blo, que
B7 E F♯m
lives with - in our strug - gles, of all the earth and
vi - ve‿en nues - tras lu - chas, del u - ni - ver - so‿en -
B7 E
heav - en the one and on - ly Lord.
te - ro el ú - ni - co Se - ñor.
E7 A
Bless - ed those who in the Lord's name an -
Ben - di - tos los que‿en su nom - bre el
B7 E F♯m
nounce the ho - ly gos - pel, pro - claim - ing the good
e - van - ge - lio‿a - nun - cian, la bue - na‿y gran no -
B7 E D.C. al fine
news that our lib - er - a - tion comes.
ti - cia de la li - be - ra - ción.

Text: Guillermo Cuéllar; tr. Linda McCrae
Music: Guillermo Cuéllar

Holy, holy holy

Santo, santo, santo

C/G Asus Am F G F/C C
Ho - ly, ho - ly, ho - ly, my heart, my heart a - dores you! My
San - to, san - to, san - to, mi cor - a - zon te a - do - ra! Mi
F G C Am F G7 C
heart is glad to say the words: you are ho - ly, Lord.
cor - a - zon te sa - be de - cir: san - to e - res Se - ñor.

Text: anonymous
Music: anonymous; arr. Pablo Sosa

63 Holy, holy, holy Lord

E B/D♯ C♯m E/B A B
Ho - ly, ho - ly, ho - ly Lord, God of pow'r and might,
E/G♯ B/F♯ E A F♯m7 B/D♯ B7
heav-en and earth are full of your glo - ry, full of your glo - ry. Ho -
E/G♯ C♯m A F♯m7 E/B C♯m E/B B
san - na, ho - san - na, ho - san - na in the high - est. Ho -
E/G♯ C♯m A F♯m/A E G♯ C♯ E B7 E F♯m7
san - na, ho - san - na, ho - san - na in the high - est.
E/G♯ A E/B Bsus G♯m A6 E/B B
Bless - ed is he who comes in the name of the Lord. Ho -

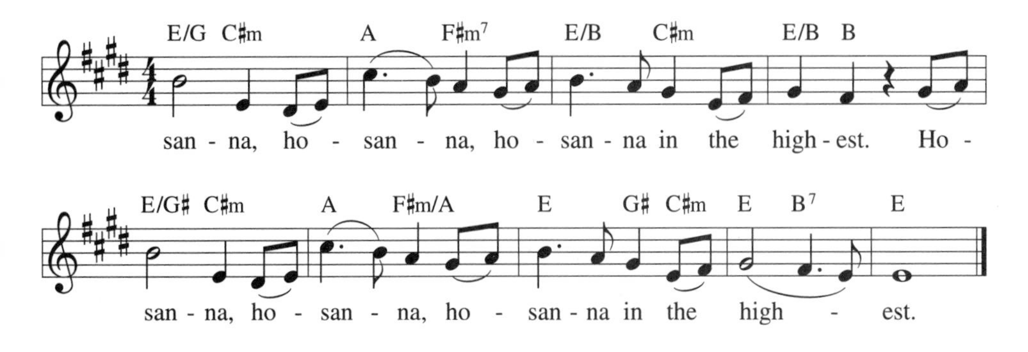
E/G C♯m A F♯m7 E/B C♯m E/B B
san - na, ho - san - na, ho - san - na in the high - est. Ho -
E/G♯ C♯m A F♯m/A E G♯ C♯m E B7 E
san - na, ho - san - na, ho - san - na in the high - est.

Text: "Sanctus," tr. English Language Liturgical Consultation
Music: Jay Beech

Holy, holy, holy Lord 64

Em F♯dim/E Em7 B7/E Em Em(♯7)
Ho - ly, ho - ly, ho - ly Lord, God of pow - er and
Em7 A9 F♯dim7 B7 Em
might, heav - en and earth are full of your
GM7 Am7 Bm7 CM7 Am7 CM7/F♯ B7
glo - ry. Ho - san - na in the high - est.
Em Em(♯7) Em7 Em6 Am9
Bless - ed is he who comes in the name of the Lord.
F♯dim Baug7 B7 F♯dim/E Em E
Ho - san - na in the high - est.

Text: "Sanctus," tr. English Language Liturgical Consultation
Music: Richard Webb and Daniel Vazquez

65
How can I be free from sin?
Lead me to the cross
1 How can I be free from sin? lead me to the cross of Jesus; from the guilt, the pow'r, the pain, lead me to the cross of Jesus.
3 How can I know peace within? lead me to the cross of Jesus; sing a song of joy again, lead me to the cross of Jesus.
5 How can I live day by day? lead me to the cross of Jesus; following his narrow way, lead me to the cross of Jesus.
Fine
2 There's no other way, no price that I could pay, simply to the cross I cling. This is all I need, this is all I plead, that his blood was shed for me.
4 Flowing from above, all-forgiving love, from the Father's heart to me. What a gift of grace, his own righteousness, clothing me in purity.
D.C.

Text and music: Graham Kendrick and Steve Thompson

How majestic is your name
66
O Lord, our Lord, how ma - jes - tic is your
name in all the earth! O Lord, our Lord, how ma -
jes - tic is your name in all the earth! O
Lord, we praise your name. O Lord,
we mag - ni - fy your name, Prince of Peace, might - y
God, O Lord God Al - might - y.

Text and music: Michael W. Smith

I love you, Lord

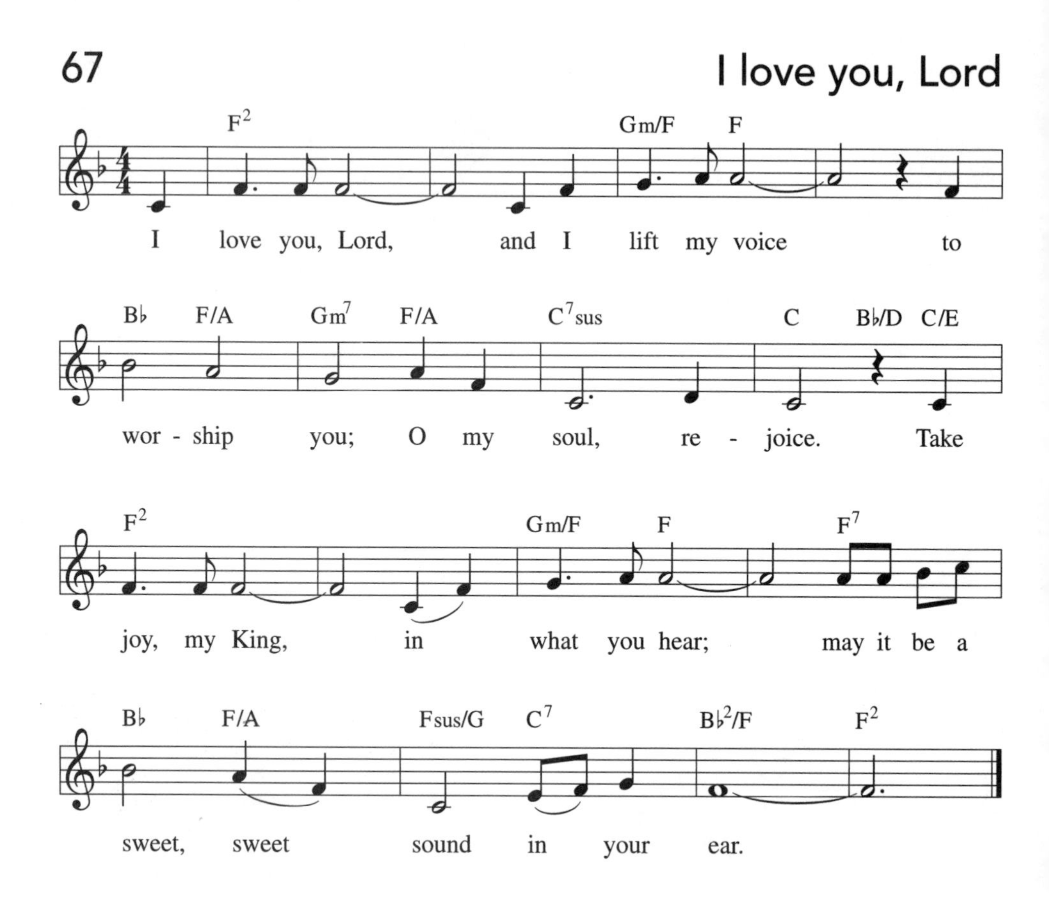
F2
Gm/F
F
I love you, Lord, and I lift my voice to
B♭
F/A
Gm7
F/A
C7sus
C
B♭/D
C/E
wor - ship you; O my soul, re - joice. Take
F2
Gm/F
F
F7
joy, my King, in what you hear; may it be a
B♭
F/A
Fsus/G
C7
B♭2/F
F2
sweet, sweet sound in your ear.

Text and music: Laurie Klein

I was glad

Refrain

I was glad when they said to me, "Let us go to the house of the Lord." I was glad when they said to me, "Let us go to the house of the Lord."

1 Called from ev - 'ry na - tion, called from ev - 'ry race,
gath - ered here for wor - ship in this ho - ly place;
God is here a - mong us, lift your hearts and sing,
make the walls and raf - ters ring. *Refrain*

2 Words that must be spo - ken, grace that must be heard,
mer - cy and for - give - ness from God's ho - ly word,
here will be re - peat - ed; peace to all pro - claimed,
shout - ed out in Je - sus' name.

3 Here the poor are wel - comed, here the lost are claimed.
Bro - ken lives are mend - ed, deep - est fears are named.
Here the wise are child - ren and the weak are strong.
Here, in Christ, we all be - long.

Text: Psalm 122:1, refrain; Jay Beech, stanzas
Music: Jay Beech

69
I was there to hear your borning cry
D7 G D G D G D7 G D G D7 G D G D G C D7sus D7 G G/B C G Am7 D7 G G/B C G A7sus2 A7 D
1 "I was there to hear your born-ing cry, I'll be there when you are old. I re-joiced the day you were bap-tized to see your life un-fold. I was there when you were but a child, with a faith to suit you well; in a blaze of light you wan-dered off to find where de-mons dwell."
2 "When you heard the won-der of the Word I was there to cheer you on; you were raised to praise the liv-ing Lord, to whom you now be-long. If you find some-one to share your time and you join your hearts as one, I'll be there to make your vers-es rhyme from dusk till ris-ing sun."
3 "In the mid-dle a-ges of your life, not too old, no lon-ger young, I'll be there to guide you through the night, com-plete what I've be-gun. When the eve-ning gent-ly clos-es in and you shut your wea-ry eyes, I'll be there as I have al-ways been, with just one more sur-prise."

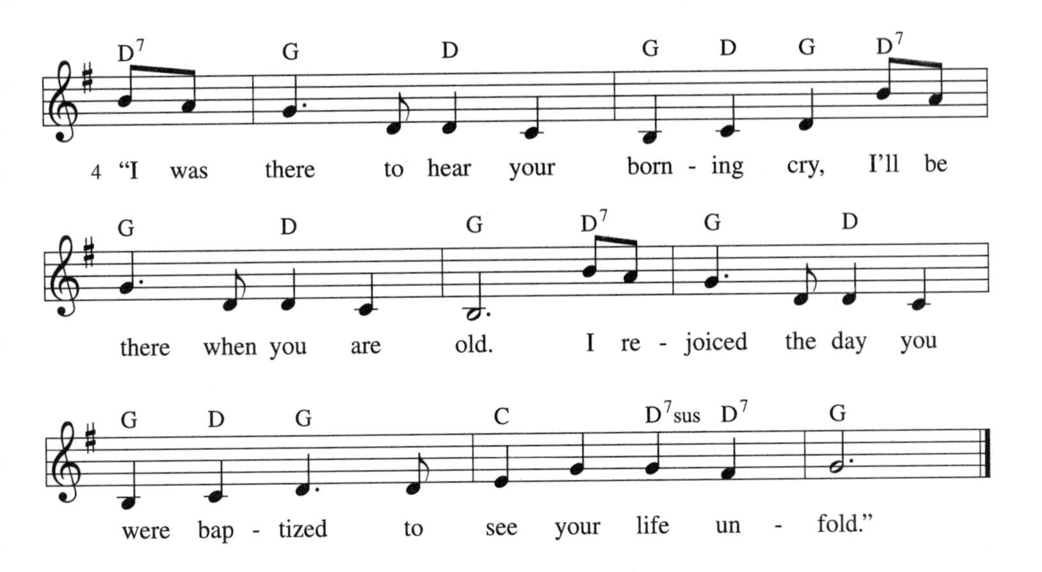
D7 G D G D G D7
4 "I was there to hear your born - ing cry, I'll be
G D G D7 G D
there when you are old. I re - joiced the day you
G D G C D7sus D7 G
were bap - tized to see your life un - fold."

Text and music: John Ylvisaker

70 I will call upon the Lord

Optional descant
I will call up - on the Lord
C F/G C F/G C F/G
I will call up - on the Lord who is wor - thy to be
who is wor - thy to be praised. So shall I be
C F/G C Gsus/C C F/C
praised. So shall I be saved from my en - e - mies.
saved from my en - e - mies.
C F/G C/G F/G C F/G
I will call up - on the Lord. The
C F C F
Lord liv - eth, and bless - ed be the Rock, and let the God of my sal -
C Gsus G C F
va - tion be ex - alt - ed. The Lord liv - eth, and bless - ed be the Rock,
C F C G7sus G7 C
and let the God of my sal - va - tion be ex - alt - ed.

Text and music: Michael O'Shields

I will celebrate

Em
C
I will cel - e - brate,
sing un - to the Lord;
D
Bm7
Em
C
D
I will sing to God a new song.
Em
C
D
Bm7
I will praise him, for he has tri - umphed vic -
1
Em
C
D
- to - rious - ly,
2
Em
C
D
Em
- to - rious - ly.

Text and music: Linda Duvall

72 I will delight

G D/F♯ Em Bm
I will de - light in the law of the Lord; I will med -
C G D/F♯
i - tate day and night. Then, like a tree firm - ly plant-
Em Bm C D G D
ed, I'll be ground - ed in your word. Bless - ed
C/D D Am/G G D/G G
is the one who fol - lows the way of the Lord;
D C D G
bless - ed is the one.

Text and music: Walt Harrah and John Schreiner

73 I will sing, I will sing

E
1 I will sing, I will sing a song un - to the Lord.
2 We will come, we will come as one be - fore the Lord.
3 If the Son, if the Son shall make . . . . . you . . . free,
4 They that sow in tears . . . . shall reap . . . . . . in . . . . joy.
5 Ev - 'ry knee shall bow . . . and ev - 'ry tongue con - fess,
6 In his name, in his name we have the vic - to - ry.

B
E
I will sing, I will sing a song un - to the Lord.
We will come, we will come as one be - fore the Lord.
if the Son, if the Son shall make . . . . . you . . . free,
They that sow in tears . . . . shall reap . . . . . . in . . . . joy.
ev - 'ry knee shall bow . . . and ev - 'ry tongue con - fess,
In his name, in his name we have the vic - to - ry.
I will sing, I will sing a song un - to the Lord.
We will come, we will come as one be - fore the Lord.
if the Son, if the Son shall make . . . . . you . . . free,
They that sow in tears . . . . shall reap . . . . . . in . . . . joy.
ev - 'ry knee shall bow . . . and ev - 'ry tongue con - fess,
In his name, in his name we have the vic - to - ry.
B
E
Al - le - lu - ia, glo - ry to the Lord.
Al - le - lu - ia, glo - ry to the Lord.
you . . . . shall be free . . . . in - deed.
Al - le - lu - ia, glo - ry to the Lord.
that . . . . Je - sus Christ . . . . is . . . . Lord.
Al - le - lu - ia, glo - ry to the Lord.
Refrain
E
Al - le - lu, al - le - lu - ia, glo - ry to the Lord. Al - le -
B
E
lu, al - le - lu - ia, glo - ry to the Lord. Al - le - lu, al - le - lu - ia, glo-
B
E
- ry to the Lord. Al - le - lu - ia, glo - ry to the Lord.

Text and music: Max Dyer

74 I will sing of the mercies of the Lord

D Em7 D/F♯ Bm7
I will sing of the mer - cies of the Lord for - ev - er, I will
Em7 A7 D G/A A7 D Em7
sing, I will sing. I will sing of the mer - cies of the
D/F♯ Bm7 Em7 A D G/D D
Fine
Lord for - ev - er, I will sing of the mer - cies of the Lord.
D7 G D
With my mouth will I make known thy
Em7 A7 G/D D D7 G
faith - ful - ness, thy faith - ful - ness. With my mouth will I make
D A/E E7 A
D.C. al fine
known thy faith - ful - ness to all gen - er - a - tions.

Text: Psalm 89:1
Music: J. H. Fillmore

In the morning

E/G♯ AM7 E
1 In the morn - ing we shall see the
2 In the eve - ning we have said, “If
3 In its cy - cle day - light dawns and
E/G♯ A B2 C♯m7 DM7
glo - ry of the Lord; rise and sing God’s prai - ses! In the
on - ly day would come, joy would spring from sor - row.” God has
night-time dark - ness parts. Day from day is sev - ered till the
AM7 E E/G♯ A B2
morn - ing we shall see our hope and faith re - stored
kept us through the night, now sha - dows will suc - cumb
Day - star of the morn - ing ri - ses in our hearts.
C♯m7 DM7 AM7 B2 AM7 E/G♯
like the sun God rais - es in the morn - ing, in the
to the new to - mor - row in the morn - ing, in the
Day will dawn for - ev - er in the morn - ing, in the
F♯m9
morn - ing.
morn - ing.
morn - ing.
Last time
E DM7 E2

Text and music: Ben Houge

76 Jesus, Lamb of God

All in all

F C/E Dm F/A B♭ F/C C
Je - sus, Lamb of God, wor - thy is your
F C F C/E Dm F/A
name; Je - sus, Lamb of God,
B♭ F/C C B♭/F F B♭/C C
wor - thy is your name.

Text and music: Dennis Jernigan, refrain of "You are my all in all"

77 Jesus, name above all names

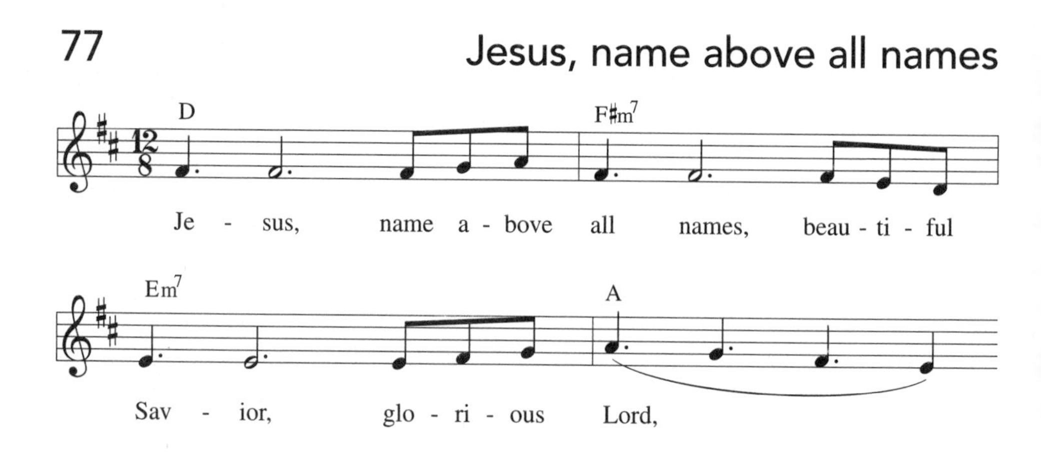
D F♯m7
Je - sus, name a - bove all names, beau - ti - ful
Em7 A
Sav - ior, glo - ri - ous Lord,

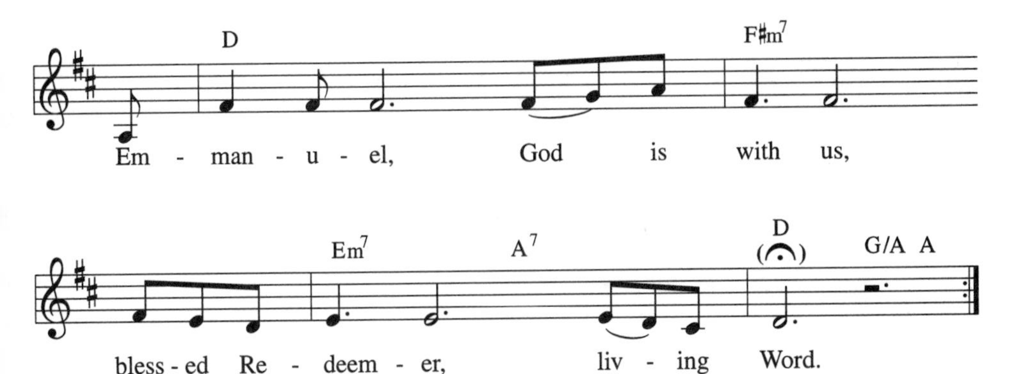
D
F♯m7
Em - man - u - el, God is with us,
Em7
A7
D
(𝄐)
G/A A
bless - ed Re - deem - er, liv - ing Word.

Text and music: Naida Hearn

Jesus, remember me

78

E♭
Fm/E♭
B♭
E♭
Je - sus, re - mem - ber me when you come in - to your king - dom.
Cm
Fm/A♭
B♭
E♭
Je - sus, re - mem - ber me when you come in - to your king - dom.

Text: Luke 23:42
Music: Jacques Berthier

79
Joyous light of glory
E2 F♯m7/E
Joy - ous light of glo - ry, shine a - mong your
CM7 DM7 Em7/D DM7 E2 Fine
peo - ple; re - flect the lov-ing face of God on high.
E2 F♯m7/E
Je - sus Christ our Sav - ior, bring us here to -
CM7 DM7 Em7/D DM7 E2
geth - er, as set-ting sun gives way to eve-ning light.
GM7 3 E2
We sing to God, Fa-ther, Son, and Spir - it,
GM7 3 E2
worth-y of praise for-ev - er and ev - er.
GM7 3 E2
O Son of God, you give us life e - ter - nal; the
CM7 DM7 Em7/D DM7 D/E E E2 D.C. al fine
u - ni-verse pro - claims your glo - ry.

Text: "Phos hilaron," adapt.
Music: Ralph C. Sappington

King of kings

1* Em
B7
Em
King of kings and Lord of lords: glo-ry, hal-le-lu-jah.
B7
Em
King of kings and Lord of lords: glo-ry, hal-le-lu-jah.
2
B7
Em
Je - sus, Prince of Peace: glo - ry, hal - le - lu - jah.
B7
Em
Je - sus, Prince of Peace: glo - ry, hal - le - lu - jah.

may be sung in canon

Text: Naomi Batya and Sophie Conty
Music: Hebrew traditional

Kyrie eleison

Refrain
Ky-ri-e e-lei-son, on our world and on our way.
Ky-ri-e e-lei-son, ev-'ry day.
Last time
1 For peace in the world, for the health of the church, for the u-ni-ty of all;
2 That we may live out your im-passioned re-sponse to the hun-gry and the poor;
3 For peace in our hearts, for peace in our homes, for friends and fam-i-ly;
4 For your Spir-it to guide; that you cen-ter our lives in the wa-ter and the word;
for this ho-ly house, for all who wor-ship and praise,
that we may live out . . . . truth and jus-tice and grace,
for life and for love, . . . for our work and our play,
that you nour-ish our souls . . . with your bo-dy and blood,
let us pray to the Lord, let us pray to the Lord.
Refrain

Kyrie eleison = Lord, have mercy

Text and music: Larry Olson

Lamb of God

Am7 GM7/A Am7 Em7/A Asus/F B♭M7
Lamb of God, you take a - way the sin of the
Asus/B D/E E Dm7 G13 CM7 B7 E7
world; have mer - cy on us.
Am7 GM7/A Am Em7/A Asus/F
Lamb of God, you take a - way the sin
B♭M7 Asus/B D/E E7 Dm7 G13 CM7
of the world; grant us peace,
B7 E7 FM7 B♭M7 Asus
grant us peace.

Text: "Agnus Dei," tr. English Language Liturgical Consultation
Music: Richard Webb and Daniel Vazquez

83

Lamb of God

Have mercy on me

A2 F♯m11 D2 E2 A F♯m11 D2 E
1 Lamb of God, you take a - way the sin of the world. Lamb of God, you take a - way the sin of the world.
2 Lamb of God, I'm ask - ing you to take a - way my sin. I con - fess that I've done wrong, I need your help a - gain.
(3) pre - cious blood of Je - sus Christ cleans - es me from sin. The pre - cious blood of Je - sus Christ cleans - es me from sin.
Refrain
A2 E/F♯ F♯m11 D D/E E A E/F♯ F♯m11 D2 E A E/F♯ F♯m11 D
Lord, have mer - cy, Christ, have mer - cy, Lord, have mer - cy on me. Lord, have mer - cy, Christ, have
Last time to coda
D/E E D/F♯ Esus E A F♯m11 D2 E D.C.
mer - cy, have mer - cy on me. 3 The
Coda
D/F♯ Esus E A F♯m11 D2 E A2
Lord, have mer - cy on me.

Text and music: Andy Park

Lead me, guide me

84

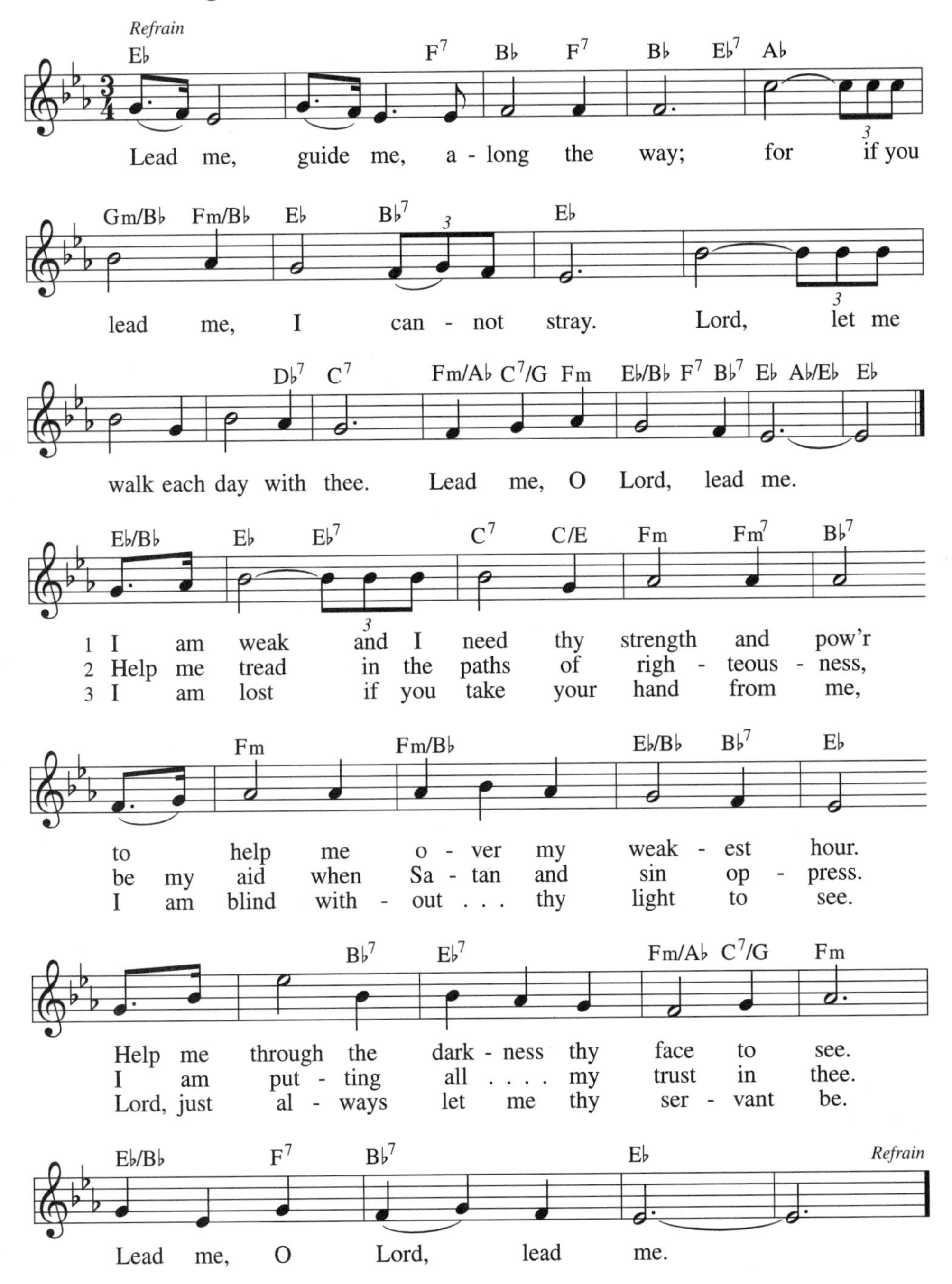
Refrain
Lead me, guide me, a - long the way; for if you
lead me, I can - not stray. Lord, let me
walk each day with thee. Lead me, O Lord, lead me.
1 I am weak and I need thy strength and pow'r
2 Help me tread in the paths of righ - teous - ness,
3 I am lost if you take your hand from me,
to help me o - ver my weak - est hour.
be my aid when Sa - tan and sin op - press.
I am blind with - out . . . thy light to see.
Help me through the dark - ness thy face to see.
I am put - ting all . . . . my trust in thee.
Lord, just al - ways let me thy ser - vant be.
Lead me, O Lord, lead me.
Refrain

Text: Doris Akers
Music: Doris Akers; arr. Richard Smallwood

85
Let justice roll like a river
Refrain
Let jus - tice roll like a riv - er, and wash all op -
pres - sion a - way. Come, O God, and take us,
move and shake us; come now, and make us a - new,
that we might live just - ly like you.
1 "Take from me your ho - ly feasts, all your
of - f'rings and your mu - sic. Let jus - tice
flow like wa - ters, and in - teg - ri - ty like an
ev - er - flow - ing stream."
Refrain

Stanzas 2-5
Gm D7/F♯ Gm Cm/G Gm Cm7
2 How long shall we wait, O God, for the day of your
3 Hear this, all of you who use the poor in your thirst of
4 "E - ven now, re - turn to me, let your hearts be
5 You have been told the way of life, the way of
F B♭ D7/A Gm D7/F♯
mer - cy to dawn, the day we beat our
pow - er and rich - es: the Lord will turn your
bro - ken and hum - ble, for I am gra - cious,
jus - tice and peace: to act just - ly, to
B♭/F Cdim/E♭ B♭/F C7/G C7 E♭/F F Refrain
swords in - to plows, when your peace reigns o - ver the earth?
laugh - ter to tears, on the won - drous Day of our God.
gen - 'rous and kind." Come and seek the mer - cies of God.
love gent - ly, to walk hum - bly with God.

Text and music: Marty Haugen

86 Let my prayer be a fragrant offering

Refrain
Am G FM7 Dm7 E7(#9) Am
Let my prayer be a fra-grant of-fer-ing, as in-cense to you a-rise.
G FM7 Dm7 G7 CM7
Let my prayer be a fra-grant of-fer-ing, my hands lift-ed up in praise.
F2 C F2 C
1 O Lord, I call to you, come quick-ly to my side.
2 Please watch my lips, O Lord, and guard the words I say.
3 My eyes are turned to you, O Lord, my liv-ing God.
F2 C G7 E7(♭9) G7 E7(♭9)
Refrain
O Lord, please hear my voice; lis-ten when I cry.
Please turn my heart to you; chase my sin a-way.
I look to you for help; be my faith-ful rock.

Text: Psalm 141, adapt.
Music: Ralph C. Sappington

Let there be praise

F C/E F Dm Dm/F Gm Gm2 Gm C
Let there be praise, let there be joy in our hearts.

Am Am7 Dm Dm/F E♭M9 E♭ Csus4/2 C
Sing to the Lord, give God the glo - ry. glo - ry.

F C/E F Dm Dm/F Gm Gm2 Gm C
Let there be praise, let there be joy in our hearts.

Am Am7 Dm Dm/F Gm F/A B♭ F/C C7 F
For - ev - er - more let his love fill the air, and let there be praise.

Text and music: Melodie Tunney and Dick Tunney

88 Lift up your heads

1 Lift up your heads, O you gates; swing wide, you
2 Up from the dead he as - cends, through ev - 'ry
3 With trum - pet blast and shouts of joy, all heav - en
ev - er - last - ing doors. Lift up your heads, O you
rank of heav'n - ly pow'r. Let heav'n pre - pare the high - est
greets the ris - en king. With an - gel choirs come line the
gates; swing wide, you ev - er - last - ing doors.
place, throw wide the ev - er - last - ing doors.
way, throw wide the gates and wel - come him.
Refrain
That the King of glo - ry may come in, that the
King of glo - ry may come in; that the King of glo - ry
may come in, that the King of glo - ry may come in.
1, 2
Last time
may come in.

Text and music: Graham Kendrick

Lord, be glorified

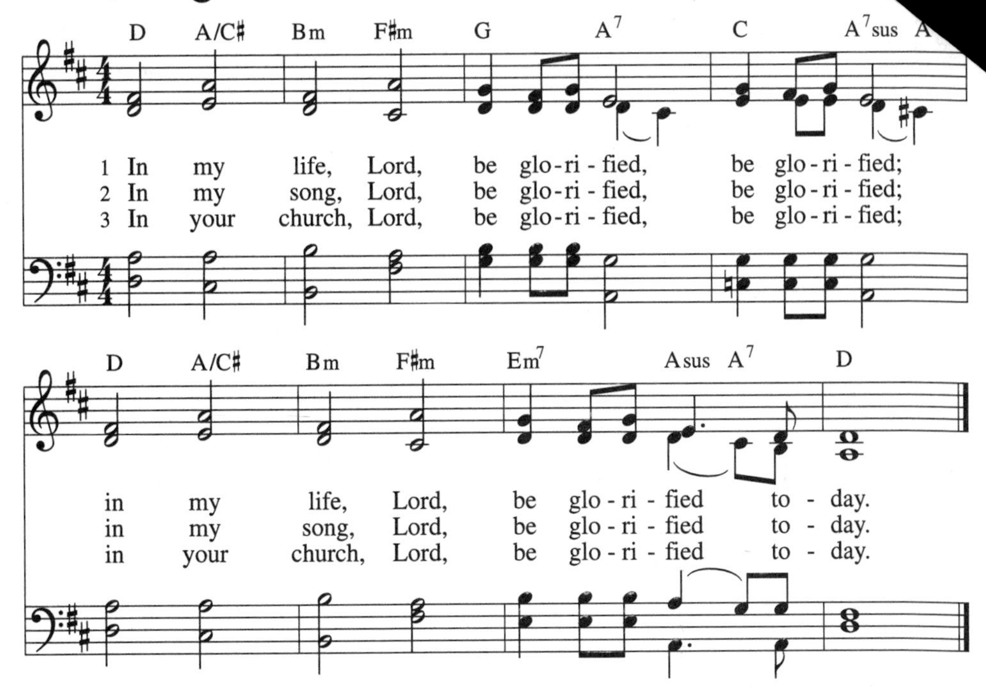
D A/C♯ Bm F♯m G A7 C A7sus A
1 In my life, Lord, be glo-ri-fied, be glo-ri-fied;
2 In my song, Lord, be glo-ri-fied, be glo-ri-fied;
3 In your church, Lord, be glo-ri-fied, be glo-ri-fied;
D A/C♯ Bm F♯m Em7 Asus A7 D
in my life, Lord, be glo-ri-fied to-day.
in my song, Lord, be glo-ri-fied to-day.
in your church, Lord, be glo-ri-fied to-day.

Text and music: Bob Kilpatrick

Lord, I lift your name on high

C D C G C
, I lift your name on high, Lord, I love to sing your
D C G C D C
prais - es. I'm so glad you're in my life,
G C Dsus D G C
I'm so glad you came to save us. You came from heav - en to earth
D C G C
to show the way, from the earth to the cross,
D C G C
my debt to pay; from the cross to the grave,
D Em7 Am7 Dsus D G C/G G
from the grave to the sky; Lord, I lift your name on high.

Lord, listen to your children

On bend-ed knee, with need-y hearts, we come and pray.
Lord, lis-ten to your chil-dren.
With will-ing hearts and o-pen arms, we come and pray.
Lord, lis-ten to your chil-dren.
With sim-ple words of heart-felt thanks, we come.
Be-liev-ing in your prom-is-es, we come.
On bend-ed knee, with need-y hearts, we come and pray.
Lord, lis-ten to your chil-dren, lis-ten to your chil-dren.

Text: Handt Hanson
Music: Handt Hanson; arr. Henry Wiens

Lord, listen to your children praying

D D7 C/G G D E7 A7
Lord, lis-ten to your chil-dren pray-ing, Lord, send your Spir-it in this place;
D D7 C/G G G♯dim7 D/A A7 G/D D
Lord, lis-ten to your chil-dren pray-ing, send us love, send us pow'r, send us grace.

Text and music: Ken Medema

Lord, my strength

F Gm7 C F
1 Lord, my strength, Lord, my rock, lead me through the dark;
2 Lord, my strength, Lord, my rock, you and you a - lone:
Gm7 C
Lord, my strength, Lord, my rock, heal this wan - d'ring heart.
Lord, my strength, Lord, my rock, lead me safe - ly home.
F Am7 D7
Be my eyes, be my ears, be the on -
Ev-'ry step that I make, be the road
Gm7 C Am7
- ly voice I hear; guide my soul, give me sight,
I will take; be the thoughts that I keep
D7 Gm7 B♭m7 C
help me walk with - in your light.
and in ev - 'ry word I speak.
F Gm7 C F
3 Lord, my strength, Lord, my rock, lead me through the dark;
Gm7 C F
Lord, my strength, Lord, my rock, heal this wan - d'ring heart.
Gm7 C7 F
Lord, my strength, Lord, my rock, you and you a - lone:
Gm7 C B♭ F
Lord, my strength, Lord, my rock, lead me safe - ly home.

Text and music: Dean Krippaehne

Majesty

G Am7 G/B C G6/B Am7 C/D D
Maj - es - ty, wor - ship his maj - es - ty: un - to
G D/F♯ Em7 A7 D7sus D7
Je - sus be all glo - ry, hon - or, and praise.
G Am7 G/B C G6/B Am7 Cm/E♭
Maj - es - ty, king - dom au - thor - i - ty flows from his
G/D Am7 D7 C/D D7 G C/G G
throne un - to his own; his an - them raise.
Bm7 B♭dim7 Am7 D7 C/D D7 G
So ex - alt, lift up on high the name of Je - sus.

G Bm7 B♭dim7 Am7 D7 C/D D7/C B
Mag - ni - fy, come glo - ri - fy Christ Je - sus, the king.
Am7 D G Am7 G/B C G6/B
Maj - es - ty, wor - ship his maj - es - ty:
Am7 Cm/E♭ G/D Am7
Je - sus who died, now glo - ri - fied,
D7 C/D D7
To repeat
G C/G G
Last time
Em Am7 Cm/E♭
King of all kings. kings. Je - sus who
G/D Am7 D7 C/D D7 G C/G G
died, now glo - ri - fied, King of all kings.

Text and music: Jack Hayford

95

Make me a channel of your peace

Prayer of St. Francis

D F#m7/C# Bm A7 Dsus2 F#m7/C#
1 Make me a chan - nel of your peace.
2 Make me a chan - nel of your peace.
4 Make me a chan - nel of your peace.
Bm A7 D F#m7/C# Bm G Asus
Where there is ha - tred, let me bring your love;
Where there's de - spair in life, let me bring hope;
It is in par - don - ing that we are par - doned,
Last time to coda
A Em2 Em Asus A Em2
where there is in - ju - ry, your par - don, Lord;
where there is dark - ness, ... on - ly light;
in giv - ing of our - selves that we re -
Asus A Em2 Em A D 1
and where there's doubt, true faith in you.
and where there's sad - ness, ev - er joy.
2 G Bm/F# Em A7 Dsus D
3 O Mas - ter, grant that I may nev - er seek so
A G Em A D2 Dsus D
much to be con - soled as to con - sole, to be
G Bm/F# Em A7 Dsus D
un - der - stood as to un - der - stand, to be

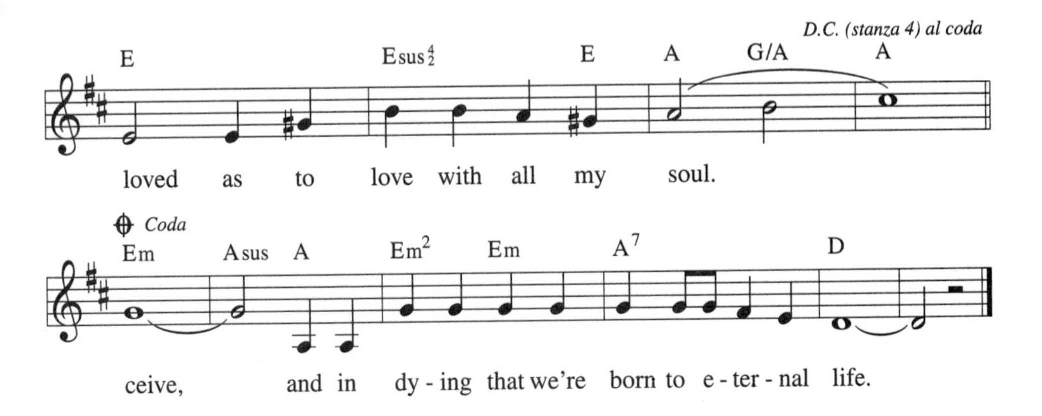
D.C. (stanza 4) al coda
loved as to love with all my soul.
Coda
ceive, and in dy - ing that we're born to e - ter - nal life.

Text and music: Sebastian Temple

Make me a servant

96

Make me a ser - vant, hum - ble and meek.
Lord, let me lift up those who are weak.
And may the prayer of my heart al - ways be:
Make me a ser - vant, make me a ser - vant,
make me a ser - vant to - day.

Text and music: Kelly Willard

97 May you run and not be weary

D G G/B D6/C C6
May you run and not be wea - ry. May your
D C/D D GM7 C/D
heart be filled with song. And may the
G G/B D6/C C6
love of God con - tin - ue to
Am7 D C/D D
give you hope and keep you strong. And may you
G G/B D6/C C6 Am
run and not be wea - ry. May your
D C/D D D/E E
life be filled with joy. And may the
Am C/D D G C/G G
road you trav - el al-ways lead you home.

Text: Handt Hanson
Music: Handt Hanson; arr. Henry Wiens

Morning has broken

C Am Dm G F C
1 Morn - ing has bro - ken like the first morn - ing;
2 Sweet the rain's new fall, sun - lit from heav - en,
3 Mine is the sun - light! Mine is the morn - ing,
Am Em Am C Dm7 G
black - bird has spo - ken like the first bird.
like the first dew - fall on the first grass.
born of the one light E - den saw play!
C Am F C Am D
Praise for the sing - ing! Praise for the morn - ing!
Praise for the sweet - ness of the wet gar - den,
Praise with e - la - tion, praise ev - 'ry morn - ing,
G C F G C
Praise for them, spring - ing fresh from the Word!
sprung in com - plete - ness where his feet pass.
God's re - cre - a - tion of the new day!

Text: Eleanor Farjeon
Music: Gaelic traditional

99 Mourning into dancing

G F♯m7(♭5) B7 D/E Em D/F♯ G Am7 G/B
You've turned my mourning into dancing again, you've
C Em7/D D G F♯m7(♭5) B7 D/E
lifted my sorrows; and I can't stay si-
Em D/F♯ G Am7 G/B Am/C C/D D G
lent, I must sing, for your joy has come.
Fine
G C G C
Where there once was only hurt, you
G C G C
gave your healing hand; where there
G C G C G C G
once was only pain, you brought comfort like a friend.
F2 C2/E
And I feel the sweetness of your love piercing my
G CM7/G G F2
darkness; and I see the bright and morning sun
C2/E F7/E♭ C/D G/D C/D D
as it ushers in your joyful gladness.
D.C. al fine

Text and music: Tommy Walker

Name above all names

E B C♯m B A
Je - sus, Je - sus, name a - bove all names, the
B
on - ly name by which we must be saved.
E B C♯m E/B A
Je - sus, Je - sus, name a - bove all names, the
F♯ A E
on - ly name by which we must be saved; the
F♯ A E
on - ly name by which we must be saved.

Text and music: Jay Beech

Night of silence

the peo - ple, win - ter of life; we
the dis - tance, call in the night; on
a - mong us, shine like the star; your
trem - ble in shad - ows this cold end - less night.
wind you en - fold us, you speak of the light.
light that guides shep - herds and kings from a - far
Fro - zen in the snow lie ros - es sleep - ing,
Gen - tle on the ear you whis - per soft - ly
shim - mer in the sky so emp - ty, lone - ly,
flow - ers that will ech - o the sun - rise;
ru - mors of a dawn so em - brac - ing;
ris - ing in the warmth of the Son's love;
fire of hope is our on - ly warmth:
breath - less love a - waits dark - ened souls:
star un - know - ing of night and day:
wea - ry, its flame will be dy - ing soon.
soon will we know of the morn - ing.
Spir - it, we wait for the lov - ing Son.

Text and music: Daniel Kantor

Silent night

A E7

1 Si - lent night, ho - ly night! All is calm,
2 Si - lent night, ho - ly night! Shep - herds quake
3 Si - lent night, ho - ly night! Son of God,

A D A

all is bright round yon vir - gin moth - er and child.
at the sight; glo - ries stream from heav - en a - far,
love's pure light ra - diant beams from your ho - ly face,

D A E

Ho - ly In - fant, so ten - der and mild, sleep in
heav'n - ly hosts . . . sing, al - le - lu - ia! Christ, the
with the dawn of re - deem - ing grace, Je - sus,

E7 A A/C♯ A E E7 A

heav - en - ly peace, sleep in heav - en - ly peace.
Sav - ior, is born! Christ, the Sav - ior, is born!
Lord, at your birth, Je - sus, Lord, at your birth.

"Silent night" may be sung simultaneously with "Night of silence." The chord symbols above are for use when "Silent night" is sung independently.

Text: Joseph Mohr, tr. John F. Young
Music: Franz Gruber

02
No longer strangers
F♯m E D E
1 We once were lost;
2 We once were cut off;
3 We who once were dead,
F♯m E D
with - out hope, with - out God; but now in Christ
but now we are brought near, for Christ is our
now we . . . live in the light, we fol - low Christ
A/C♯ A E/G♯ A/F♯ E
Je - sus, we have been found—
peace, . . . we were bro - ken, now whole— one
Je - sus, a - bun - dant in grace— who
Bm7 A/C♯ Bm A/C♯ D/E E
saved by the prom - ise of God!
spir - it, one bod - y of Christ!
saved us, who raised us to life!
Refrain
A C♯m7 D E E/G♯ A E/G♯ F♯m7
No long - er stran - gers, no long - er lost and a - lone!
D D/E E A C♯m7 D E
No long - er stran - gers, now we are
F♯m E D D/E E A
saints! We are one in the house of God!

Text: David Haas
Music: David Haas; arr. Jeanne Cotter

Now God our Father

C F/C C F/C C
1 Now God our Fa - ther, you are the pot - ter;
2 All of cre - a - tion in cel - e - bra - tion,
F/C C B♭ F/A C F/C C
we are the work of your hands. Mold us and make us,
prais - ing the God of all life, bless - ing their mak - er,
F/C C F/C C B♭ F/A
make us like Je - sus; we are the work of your hands.
mas - ter, cre - a - tor; prais - ing the God of all life.
Refrain
F G/F F C2/E F G Am G
Be glo - ri - fied, God of our lives; be glo - ri - fied in us.
F G/F F C2/E F G Csus C
Be glo - ri - fied, God of our lives; be glo - ri - fied in us.

Text: Kirk Dearman
Music: Jim Mills

Now in this banquet

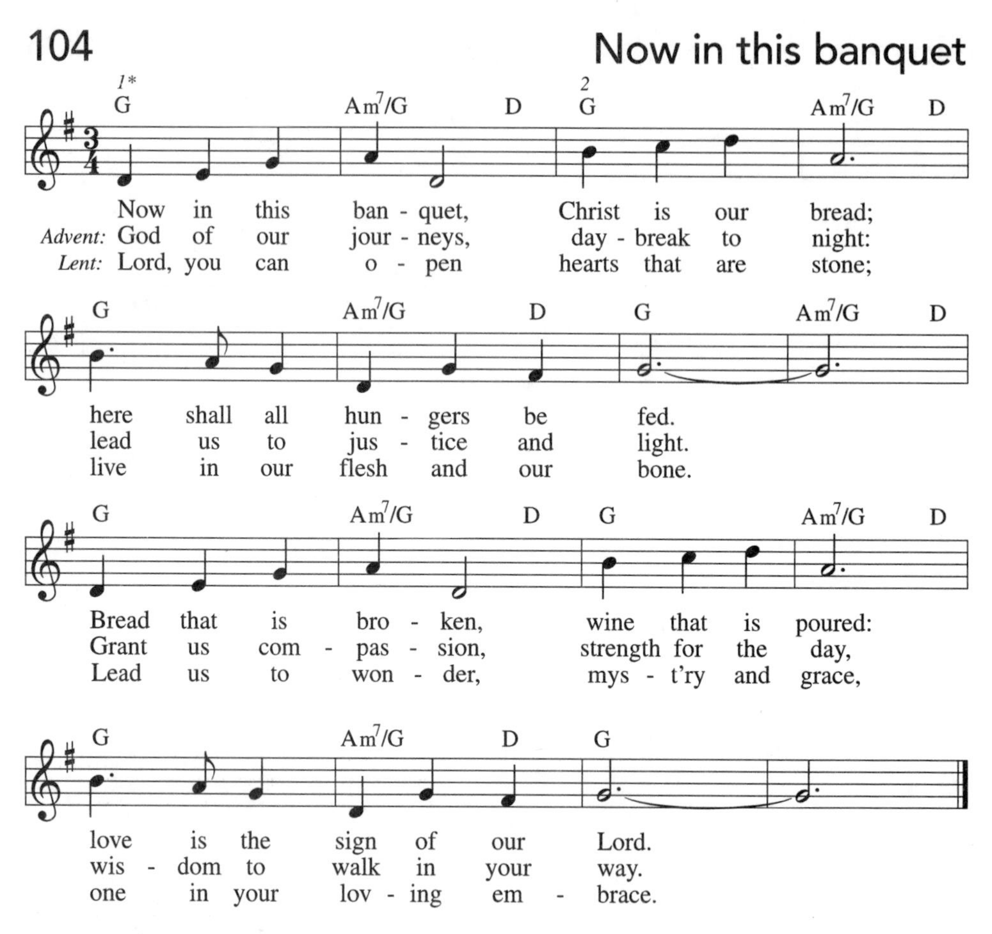
1* 2
G Am7/G D G Am7/G D
Now in this ban - quet, Christ is our bread;
Advent: God of our jour - neys, day - break to night:
Lent: Lord, you can o - pen hearts that are stone;
G Am7/G D G Am7/G D
here shall all hun - gers be fed.
lead us to jus - tice and light.
live in our flesh and our bone.
G Am7/G D G Am7/G D
Bread that is bro - ken, wine that is poured:
Grant us com - pas - sion, strength for the day,
Lead us to won - der, mys - t'ry and grace,
G Am7/G D G
love is the sign of our Lord.
wis - dom to walk in your way.
one in your lov - ing em - brace.

**may be sung in canon*

Soloist or choir:

1 You who have touched us and graced us with love,
make us your people of goodness and light.

2 Let our hearts burn with the fire of your love;
open our eyes to the glory of God.

3 God who makes the blind to see, God who makes the lame to walk,
bring us dancing into day, lead your people in your way

4 Hope for the hopeless, light for the blind:
"Strong" is your name, Lord, "Gentle" and "Kind."

5 Call us to be your light, call us to be your love,
make us your people again.

6 Come, O Spirit! Renew our hearts!
We shall arise to be children of light.

Text and music: Marty Haugen

Now the day has drawn to a close

D2 Am9
Now the day has drawn to a close;
D2 G2
both the night and day are yours.
D2 Am9
In our dark - ness, give us your light;
Bm7 Em7
let your bright face shine on us.
D2 Am9
Be a light un - to our feet;
GM7 CM7 Am9 D2
make the eve - ning shad - ows flee. A - men

The phrases of this song may be sung in alternation between leader and congregation.

Text and music: Ben Houge

106 Now we remain

Refrain
Gsus G G2 G D/F♯ C/G
We hold the death of the Lord deep in our
G G/F♯ Em Em7/D C G/B
hearts. Liv - ing, now we re - main with
Am7 D Gsus G2 Gsus G G2 G
Je - sus the Christ.
Gsus G G2 G D/F♯ C/G
1 Once we were peo - ple a - fraid, lost in the
G D/F♯ Em Em7/D C G/B
night. Then by your cross we were saved;
Am7 G/B C C/D D Refrain
dead be - came liv - ing, life from your giv - ing.
Gsus G G2 G D/F♯ C/G
2 Some - thing which we have known, some - thing we've
G D/F♯ Em Em7/D C
touched, what we have seen with our eyes,

Am7 G/B C C/D D Refrain
this we have heard: life - giv - ing Word.
Gsus G G2 G D/F♯ C/G
3 He chose to give of him - self, be - came our
G D/F♯ Em Em7/D C
bread; bro - ken, that we might live;
Am7 G/B C C/D D Refrain
love be - yond love, pain for our pain.
Gsus G G2 G D/F♯ C/G
4 We are the pres - ence of God; this is our
G D/F♯ Em Em7/D C G/B Am7
call; now to be - come bread and wine, food for the
G/B C C/D D
hun - gry, life for the wea - ry; for to
Am7 G/B F C/E C/D D Refrain
live with the Lord, we must die with the Lord.

Text and music: David Haas

107 Oh, come, let us sing

Refrain
Oh, come, let us sing to the Lord; let us shout for joy to the rock of our sal-va-tion! Oh, come, let us sing to the Lord; let us shout for joy to the rock of our sal-va-tion!
Last time to coda
1 Oh, come, of-fer thank-ful-ness to God. Let us raise a glad shout to God with psalms. For the Lord is a great and might-y God rul-ing high o-ver all.
2 Your hands hold the cav-erns of the earth, and the heights of the hills be-long to you. Your hands have cre-a-ted the vast sea, and you formed the dry land.
3 Oh, come, let us wor-ship and bow down; let us kneel be-fore our cre-a-tor, God. We are yours, the . . . peo-ple of your field and the sheep of your hand.
Refrain
Coda
our sal-va-tion!

Text: "Venite," Psalm 95:1-7a, adapt.
Music: Ben Hougе

O Lord, hear our prayer 108

CM7 D G
O Lord, hear our prayer we of - fer up to
CM7 D G
you; O Lord, hear our prayer.

Text and music: Ralph C. Sappington

O Lord, my heart is not proud 109

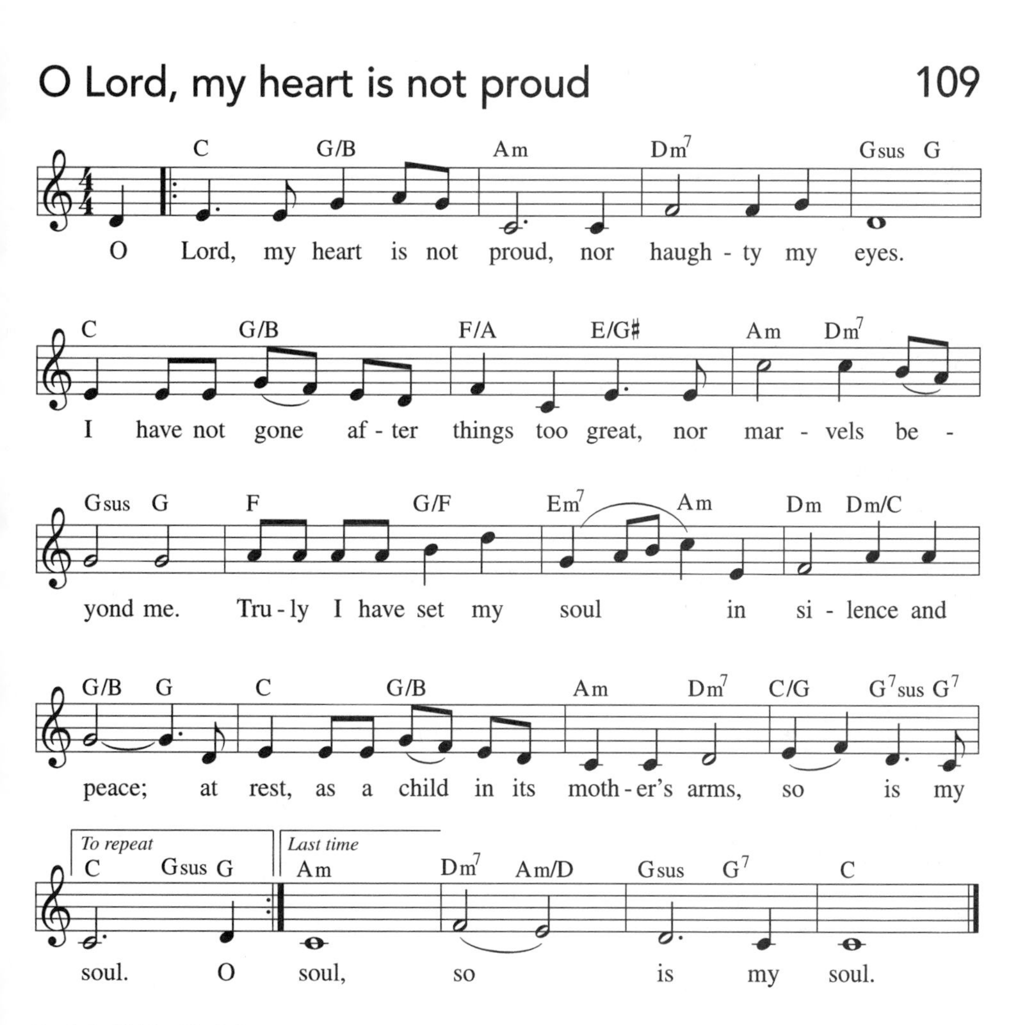

C G/B Am Dm7 Gsus G
O Lord, my heart is not proud, nor haugh - ty my eyes.
C G/B F/A E/G♯ Am Dm7
I have not gone af - ter things too great, nor mar - vels be -
Gsus G F G/F Em7 Am Dm Dm/C
yond me. Tru - ly I have set my soul in si - lence and
G/B G C G/B Am Dm7 C/G G7sus G7
peace; at rest, as a child in its moth - er's arms, so is my
To repeat
C Gsus G
soul. O
Last time
Am Dm7 Am/D Gsus G7 C
soul, so is my soul.

Text: Psalm 131:1-2, tr. The Grail
Music: Margaret Rizza

110
On eagle's wings
G F♯m7 Bm
1 You who dwell in the shel - ter of the Lord, who a -
G F♯m7 F
bide in his shad - ow for life, say to the Lord: "My
Dm F Gm Asus
ref - uge, my rock in whom I trust!"
Refrain
A D
And he will raise you up on ea - gle's wings,
Em A7 D D7/F♯
bear you on the breath of dawn, make you to shine like the
To stanzas
(last time to coda)
G Em A Bm F♯ Em A7 D
sun, and hold you in the palm of his hand.
G F♯m7 Bm
2 The snare of the fowl - er will nev - er cap - ture you, and
G F♯m7 F
fam - ine will bring you no fear; un - der his wings your
3

Dm F Gm Asus Refrain
ref - uge, his faith - ful - ness your shield.
D G 3 F♯m7 Bm
3 You need not fear the ter - ror of the night, nor the
G F♯m7 F
ar - row that flies by day; though thou - sands fall a -
Dm F Gm Asus Refrain
bout you, near you it shall not come.
D G 3 DM7 Bm
4 For to his an - gels he's giv - en a com - mand to
G F♯m7 F
guard you in all of your ways; up - on their hands they will
Gm9 Am B♭ Asus Refrain
bear you up, lest you dash your foot a - gainst a stone.
Coda
D Bm F♯m Em A7sus A D
And hold you, hold you in the palm of his hand.

Text and music: Michael Joncas

111 One bread, one body

Refrain
One bread, one bod-y, one Lord of all;
one cup of bless-ing which we bless, and
we, though man-y through-out the earth,
we are one bod-y in this one Lord.
1 Gen-tile or Jew, ser-vant or free,
2 Man-y the gifts, man-y the works,
3 Grain for the fields, scat-tered and grown,
wom-an or man, no more.
one in the Lord of all.
gath-ered to one for all.
Refrain

Text and music: John Foley

Only by grace

C G/C C Dm7
On-ly by grace can we en - ter, on - ly by grace can we stand;
Gsus G C G/C C
not by our hu - man en - deav - or,
Dm7 F/G G Em7
but by the blood of the Lamb. In - to your pres - ence you call
G/A Am FM7 Gsus G
us, you call us to come.
C G/A Am7 Dm7 G
In - to your pres - ence you draw us, and now by your grace we come,
C Am7 Dm7 G C Fine
now by your grace we come.
G/B Am G F F/G G
Lord, if you mark our trans - gres - sions, who would
G/C C Dm/B E7 Am G
stand? Thanks to your grace we are cleansed
D.C. al fine
F G Am Dm7 E7 F/G Gsus G
by the blood of the Lamb.

Text and music: Gerrit Gustafson

113 Open our eyes, Lord

D G2 G Em7/A A7
O - pen our eyes, Lord; we want to see
G/D D A/C♯ Bm D/A GM9
Je - sus, to reach out and touch
Em A7 G/D D2 D
him, and say that we love him.
DM7 A/G G Em7 A7
O - pen our ears, Lord, and help us to
G/D D A Bm7 D/A GM9
lis - ten. O - pen our eyes,
Em7 A7 D
Lord, we want to see Je - sus.

Text and music: Bob Cull

114 Our confidence is in the Lord

C F C
Our con - fi - dence is in the Lord, the source of our sal -
FM7 G C F C
va - tion. Rest is found in God a - lone, the

F G Am Em/G
au - thor of cre - a - tion. We will not fear the e -
F C Am Em/G F G
- vil day, be - cause we have a ref - uge;
Am Em/G F C F G
in ev - 'ry cir - cum - stance we say, our hope is built on Je - sus.
C/E Dm7
God is our for - tress, we will nev - er be shak - en.
C/E F
God is our for - tress, we will nev - er be shak - en.
C/E Dm7
God is our for - tress, we will nev - er be shak - en.
C/E F
God is our for - tress, we will nev - er be shak - en.
G Am Am/G
We will put our trust in God.
F G C/E C
We will put our trust in God.

Text and music: Noel Richards and Tricia Richards

115 Out in the wilderness

Em A9/E Em7 A9/E Am Baug7 Em A9/E
1 Driv - en by the Spir - it out in the wil - der - ness;
2 Tempt-ed by the dev - il out in the wil - der - ness;
3 An - gels all a - round you out in the wil - der - ness;
4 "You are my be - lov - ed" out in the wil - der - ness.
Em A9/E Em7 A9/E C B7
driv - en by the Spir - it out in the wil - der - ness;
tempt - ed by the dev - il out in the wil - der - ness;
an - gels all a - round you out in the wil - der - ness;
"You are my be - lov - ed" out in the wil - der - ness.
Em A9/E Em7 A9/E
when the Spir - it says, "Go," you can't say, "No."
though you try to be strong, it's been so long.
you are far . . . . from home where wild things roam.
When you were . . . bap - tized, you re - a - lized
F B7 B7(♭5)/F
You lis - ten for the voice when you're bend - ed low;
He whis - pers in your ear and you know he's wrong;
There's dan - ger ev - 'ry - where but you're not a - lone;
you'd heard the voice of God from the o - p'ning skies:
Em A9/E Em7 A9/E Am Baug7 Em
driv - en by the Spir - it out in the wil - der - ness.
tempt - ed by the dev - il out in the wil - der - ness.
an - gels all a - round you out in the wil - der - ness.
"You are my be - lov - ed" out in the wil - der - ness.

Text and music: Jay Beech

Praise, praise, praise the Lord

Praise, praise, praise the Lord! Praise God's ho - ly name. Al - le - lu - ia!
Praise, praise, praise the Lord! Praise God's ho - ly name. Al - le - lu - ia!
Praise God's ho - ly name. Al - le - lu - ia! Praise God's ho - ly name. Al - le - lu - ia!
Praise God's ho - ly name. Al - le - lu - ia! Praise God's ho - ly name. Al - le - lu - ia!

This song may be repeated, adding a vocal part on each repetition: melody (alto) alone; melody + tenor; melody + lower parts; all voices.

Text: traditional; collected by Elaine Hanson
Music: Cameroon processional; arr. Ralph M. Johnson

117 Praise the name of Jesus

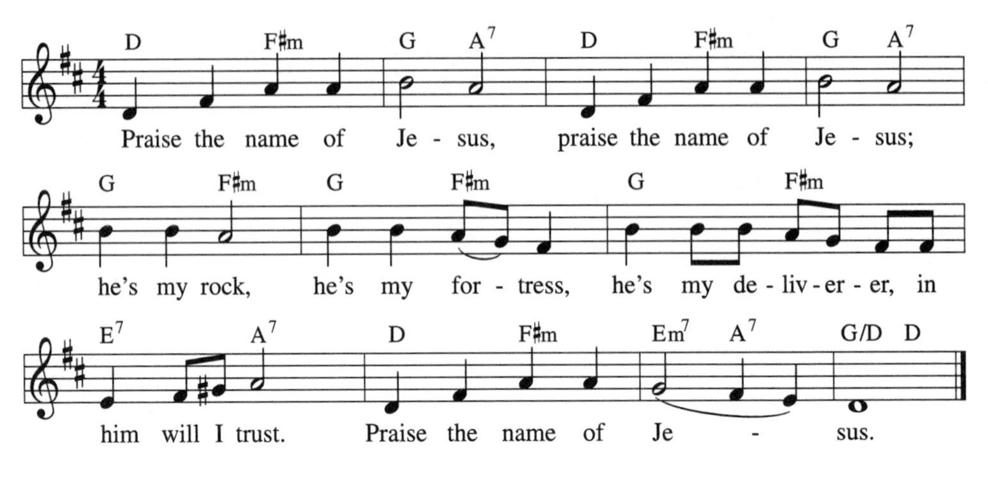

Praise the name of Je - sus, praise the name of Je - sus;
he's my rock, he's my for - tress, he's my de - liv - er - er, in
him will I trust. Praise the name of Je - sus.

Text and music: Roy Hicks Jr.

118 Praise to you, O Christ, our Savior

Refrain
Praise to you, O Christ, our Sav - ior, Word of the Fa-ther, call-ing us to life;
Son of God who leads us to free-dom: glo - ry to you, Lord Je-sus Christ!
1 You are the Word who calls us out of dark - ness;
2 You are the one whom proph - ets hoped and longed for;
3 You are the Word who calls us to be ser - vants;
4 You are the Word who binds us and u - nites us;
you are the Word who leads us in - to light; you are the Word who
you are the one who speaks to us to - day; you are the one who
you are the Word whose on - ly law is love; you are the Word made
you are the Word who calls us to be one; you are the Word who

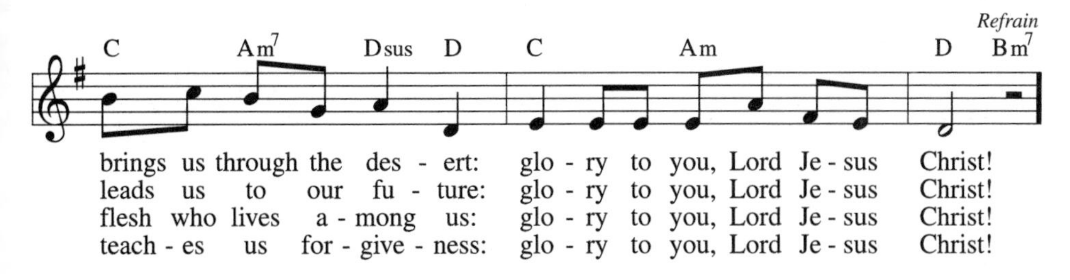
Refrain
C Am7 Dsus D C Am D Bm7
brings us through the des - ert: glo - ry to you, Lord Je - sus Christ!
leads us to our fu - ture: glo - ry to you, Lord Je - sus Christ!
flesh who lives a - mong us: glo - ry to you, Lord Je - sus Christ!
teach - es us for - give - ness: glo - ry to you, Lord Je - sus Christ!

Text and music: Bernadette Farrell

Praise to you, O God of mercy 119

E B/D♯ A/C♯ E/B B A F♯m E/G♯
1 Praise to you, O God of mer - cy! Thanks be to you for -
2 From of old you loved and sought us! Thanks be to you for -
3 Praise to you, O God of mer - cy! Thanks be to you for -
Last time to coda
E/B B7 E/G♯ A F♯m7 G♯7 A F♯m7
ev - er! Rais - ing high the weak and low - ly: thanks be to you for -
ev - er! Truth and jus - tice you have taught us: thanks be to you for -
ev - er! Rais - ing high the weak and low - ly: thanks be to you for -
1 B7 E 2 B7 E A B/A E/G♯ C♯m
ev - er! ev - er! Strong is your faith - ful - ness,
F♯m G♯7 C♯m E7/B A B/A E/G♯ C♯m
strong is your love, re - mem - b'ring your cov - e - nant of
To stanza 3 Coda
D F♯m/C♯ Bsus B7 B7 C♯m A F♯m7 B7 E
life with us. ev - er! Thanks be to you for - ev - er!

Text and music: Marty Haugen

Rejoice in the mission

E♭ B♭ E♭ E♭sus E♭
1 Oh, the Lord came down from heav'n, ti - ny
2 As we pon - der and we plan in this
A♭ B♭7 E♭ A♭ Gm/B♭
ba - by, great phy - si - cian, gave his bod - y and his
age of great tran - si - tion, we will keep the word of
Cm Fm7 A♭/B♭
blood to live out a ho - ly mis - sion.
God at the heart of each de - ci - sion.
B♭ E♭ E♭sus E♭
His dis - ci - ples, they went out to ful -
Praise the Fa - ther, Lord of love; praise the
A♭ B♭/A♭ Gm7 Cm7 Fm7 Gm7
fill the great com - mis - sion; with a seed of faith so
Christ, in glo - ry ris - en; praise the Spir - it, by whose
A♭2 Fm7/D♭
small, learned a dif - f'rent kind of
pow'r we will share the gifts we're
Fm7/B♭ B♭ E♭ E♭sus E♭
fish - in'. Will we go?
giv - en— as we go.

Refrain
A♭ B♭7 E♭
And we'll all share the vi - sion, who in
A♭ Gm7 Cm Fm Gm
Christ we all shall be. Come, re - joice in the
Cm/A♭ A♭/B♭ B♭
mis - sion of a new com - mu - ni - ty.
E♭ A♭ Fm/A♭ Cm E♭/B♭
In this place where we ga - ther, Je - sus,
A♭ B♭ C2 Fm7
still our rest - less souls; to your Spir - it we will
A♭/D♭ A♭/B♭ B♭ E♭
lis - ten. We will go.

Text: Dan Bielenberg
Music: Appalachian traditional, adapt. and arr. Dori Erwin Collins

121 Seed, scattered and sown

Refrain
Seed, scat-tered and sown; wheat, gath-ered and grown;
bread, bro-ken and shared as one, the Liv-ing Bread of God.
Vine, fruit of the land; wine, work of our hands; one cup that is
shared by all; the Liv-ing Cup, the Liv-ing Bread of God.
1 Is not the bread we break a shar-ing in our Lord? Is not the cup we bless the blood of Christ out-poured?
2 The seed which falls on rock will with-er and will die. The seed with-in good ground will flow-er and have life.
3 As wheat up-on the hills was gath-ered and was grown, so may the church of God be gath-ered in-to one.
Refrain

Text: Dan Feiten
Music: Dan Feiten; arr. Eric Gunnison and R. J. Miller

Seek ye first

Optional descant
Al - le - lu - ia, al - le - lu - ia, al - le - lu - ia, al - le - lu - ia.
D F♯m G D G D Em7 A7 D F♯m G D G D Em7 A D
1 Seek ye first the king - dom of God and its righ - teous - ness, and all these things shall be add - ed un - to you. Al - le - lu, al - le - lu - ia.
2 Ask and it shall be giv - en un - to you; seek and you shall find; knock and the door shall be o - pened un - to you. Al - le - lu, al - le - lu - ia.

Text: Matthew 6:33, 7:7; adapt. Karen Lafferty
Music: Karen Lafferty

123 Shine, Jesus, shine

Refrain
A E/A D A/C♯ Bm B7
Shine, Je - sus, shine, fill this land with the
E A E/A D A
Fa - ther's glo - ry; blaze, Spir - it, blaze, set our
Bm Bm/A G E A E/A D A/C♯
hearts on fire. Flow, riv - er, flow, flood the
Bm B7 E A E/A
na - tions with grace and mer - cy; send forth your Word,
D A/C♯ Bm E7 A D
To stanzas
E/A D/A
Last time
A
Lord, and let there be light!
A D/A A E/A
1 Lord, the light of your love is shin - ing,
2 As we gaze on your king - ly bright - ness,
A D/A A E/A
in the midst of the dark - ness, shin - ing;
so our fac - es dis - play your like - ness,

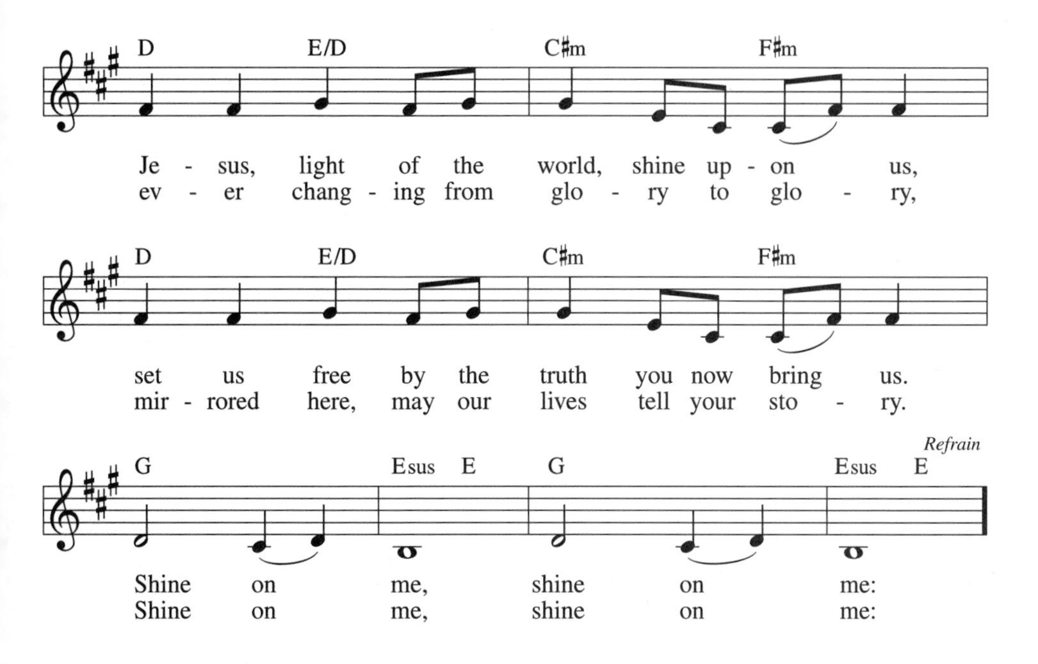
D E/D C♯m F♯m
Je - sus, light of the world, shine up - on us,
ev - er chang - ing from glo - ry to glo - ry,
D E/D C♯m F♯m
set us free by the truth you now bring us.
mir - rored here, may our lives tell your sto - ry.
Refrain
G Esus E G Esus E
Shine on me, shine on me:
Shine on me, shine on me:

Text and music: Graham Kendrick

Shout to the Lord
A E F♯m E
My Je - sus, my Sav - ior, Lord, there is none like you.
D A/C♯ D A/E F♯m7
All of my days I want to praise the won - ders of your
G D/F♯ Esus E D/E A E
might - y love. My com - fort, my shel - ter,
F♯m E D
tow - er of ref - uge and strength; let ev - 'ry breath,
A/C♯ D A/E F♯m G D/F♯ Esus E
all that I am nev - er cease to wor - ship you.

A F♯m D D/E E
Shout to the Lord, all the earth, let us sing
A F♯m D Esus E
pow-er and maj - es - ty, praise to the King.
F♯m D E F♯m
Moun-tains bow down and the seas will roar at the sound of your
E/G♯ A F♯m D D/E E
name. I sing for joy at the work of your hands; for -
A F♯m D Esus E
ev - er I'll love you, for - ev - er I'll stand.
F♯m D D/E E A
Noth-ing com - pares to the prom - ise I have in you.

Text and music: Darlene Zschech

Sing a new song

Refrain
G D B7 Em Am7
Sing a new song un - to the Lord; let your song be
D G D
sung from moun - tains high. Sing a new song
B7 Em Am7 D G Fine
un - to the Lord, sing-ing al - le - lu - ia.
G D7/A Am7/G D/F♯ Em
1 Yah - weh's peo - ple dance for joy; oh, come be -
2 Rise, O chil - dren, from your sleep; your Sav - ior
3 Glad my soul, for I have seen the glo - ry
Am7/C D7/A D/F♯ G D7/A
fore the Lord, and praise the Lord on
now has come. The Lord has turned your
of the Lord. The trum - pet sounds; the
Am7/G D C Am7 Dsus D Refrain
glad tam - bou - rines, and let your trum - pet sound.
sor - row to joy, and filled your soul with song.
dead shall be raised. I know my Sav - ior lives.

Text and music: Daniel Schutte

Sing out, earth and skies

Leader
D G D
All
Am7
1 Come, O God of all the earth: come to us, O
2 Come, O God of wind and flame: fill the earth with
3 Come, O God of flash - ing light: twin - kling star and
4 Come, O God of snow and rain: show - er down up -
5 Come, O Jus - tice, come, O Peace: come and shape our
F D
Leader
D G D
Righ - teous One; come, and bring our love to birth:
righ - teous - ness; teach us all to sing your name:
burn - ing sun; God of day and God of night:
on the earth; come, O God of joy and pain:
hearts a - new; come and make op - pres - sion cease:
All
Am7 F D
in the glo - ry of your Son.
may our lives your love con - fess.
in your light we all are one.
God of sor - row, God of mirth.
bring us all to life in you.
Refrain
D G/D D G/D D
Sing out, earth and skies! Sing of the God who
A/D D G/D D
loves you! Raise your joy - ful cries!
C Am7 D C Am7 D
Dance to the life a - round you!

Text and music: Marty Haugen

Song over the waters

Refrain
Dm7/G G2 Dm7/G
God, you have moved up - on the wa - ters, you have sung in the
G2 Dm7/G
rush of wind and flame; and in your love you have called us sons and
G2 Dm7/G Last time to coda G2
daugh - ters: make us peo - ple of the wa - ter and your name.
Am7 G/B
1 Come fill our wait - ing hearts with the spir - it of
2 Give us a thirst for love, give us a hun - ger for
3 You are the breath of life, you are the hope of the
4 Come, o - pen ev - 'ry heart, come now and wake us to
C E♭ Dm7 G2 Refrain
Je - sus, let us shine with your light and peace.
jus - tice, make us one with the mind of Christ.
hope - less, come and fill us with light and peace.
won - der, make us ves - sels of light and peace.
Coda
G2 Dm7/G G2
name. Make us peo - ple of the wa - ter and your name.

Text and music: Marty Haugen

Soon and very soon

F Bb/F F
1 Soon and ver - y soon
2 No more cry - in' there,
3 No more dy - in' there,
4 Soon and ver - y soon
we are goin' to see the King,
C7 F
soon and ver - y soon
no more cry - in' there,
no more dy - in' there,
soon and ver - y soon
we are goin' to see the King,
Bb/F F
soon and ver - y soon
no more cry - in' there,
no more dy - in' there,
soon and ver - y soon
we are goin' to see the King.
F7 Bb Bbm7 F/C C7
1, 2
F
Hal - le - lu - jah, hal - le - lu - jah, we're goin' to see the King!
3, 4
F G7 C7 F G7 C7
Hal - le - lu - jah, hal - le - lu -
F G7 C7 F G7 C7 F
jah, hal - le - lu - jah, hal - le - lu - jah.

Text and music: Andraé Crouch

Spirit of the living God

F Gm7/B♭ D/A Gm F/C C7 F
Spir - it of the liv - ing God, fall fresh on me,
F Gm7/B♭ D/A Gm F/C C7 F
Spir - it of the liv - ing God, fall fresh on me.
B♭ F G7 C F/C C7
Melt me, mold me, fill me, use me.
F Gm7/B♭ D/A Gm F/C C7 F
Spir - it of the liv - ing God, fall fresh on me.

Text and music: Daniel Iverson

Spirit song

D GM7 Bm/F♯ Em7 A A/G F♯m7
Oh, let the Son of God en - fold you with his Spir - it and his
Bm7 Em7 A7 DM7
love, let him fill your heart and sat - is - fy your soul.
Em7 F♯m7 GM7 Bm/F♯ Em7 A A/G F♯m7
Oh, let him have the things that hold you, and his Spir - it like a
Bm7 Em7 Em7/A G/A A D C/E D/F♯
dove will de - scend up - on your life and make you whole.
Refrain
GM7 A/G F♯m7 Bm7 Em7
Je - sus, O Je - sus, come and
A DM7 C/E D/F♯ GM7 A A/G
fill your lambs. Je - sus, O
F♯m7 Bm7 Em7 Asus7 A7 D
Je - sus, come and fill your lambs.

Text and music: John Wimber

131 Stand in the congregation

E♭ Fm/E♭ E♭ Fm/E♭ E♭ Fm/E♭
1 I will stand in the con - gre - ga - tion and I will ex - alt you; I will stand in the con - gre - ga - tion and I will ex - alt you. Let the chil - dren of your sal - va - tion lift their prais - es too!
2 I will stand in the con - gre - ga - tion and I will . . . praise your name; I will stand in the con - gre - ga - tion and I will . . . praise your name. With your peo - ple in ev - 'ry na - tion I will shout this praise!
3 We will join as a con - gre - ga - tion and we will ex - alt you; we will join as a con - gre - ga - tion and we will ex - alt you. We will sing . . . as all cre - a - tion lifts the song a - new!
E♭ Fm/E♭ E♭ B♭ B♭7
A♭/B♭ E♭ Fm/E♭ E♭ Fm/E♭
E♭ Fm/E♭ E♭ Fm/E♭ E♭ E♭7/G A♭
Fm7 E♭ A♭M7/B♭ B♭7 E♭ Fm/B♭
1, 2
E♭
Hal - le - lu - jah!

3
E♭ B♭sus B♭ Gm7 Cm7
Hal - le - lu - jah! Hal - le - lu - jah!
Fsus F B♭ A♭/B♭ B♭
Hal - le - lu - jah! Hal - le - lu - jah!
A♭/B♭ B♭ E♭ Fm/E♭ E♭ Fm/E♭
Let the chil - dren of your sal - va - tion lift their
E♭ E♭7/G A♭ Fm7 E♭ A♭M7/B♭ B♭7 E♭ Fm/B♭ E♭
prais - es too! Hal - le - lu - jah!

Text and music: Bill Batstone

132
Step by step
O God, you are my God, and I will ev - er praise you. O God, you are my God, and
I will ev - er praise you. I will seek you in the morn-
- ing, and I will learn to walk in your ways, and
step by step you'll lead me, and I will fol - low you all of my
days. O days, and I will fol - low you all of my
days, and I will fol - low you all of my days, and
step by step you'll lead me, and I will fol - low you all of my days.

Text: Beaker
Music: Beaker; arr. Nylea Butler-Moore

That Christ be known

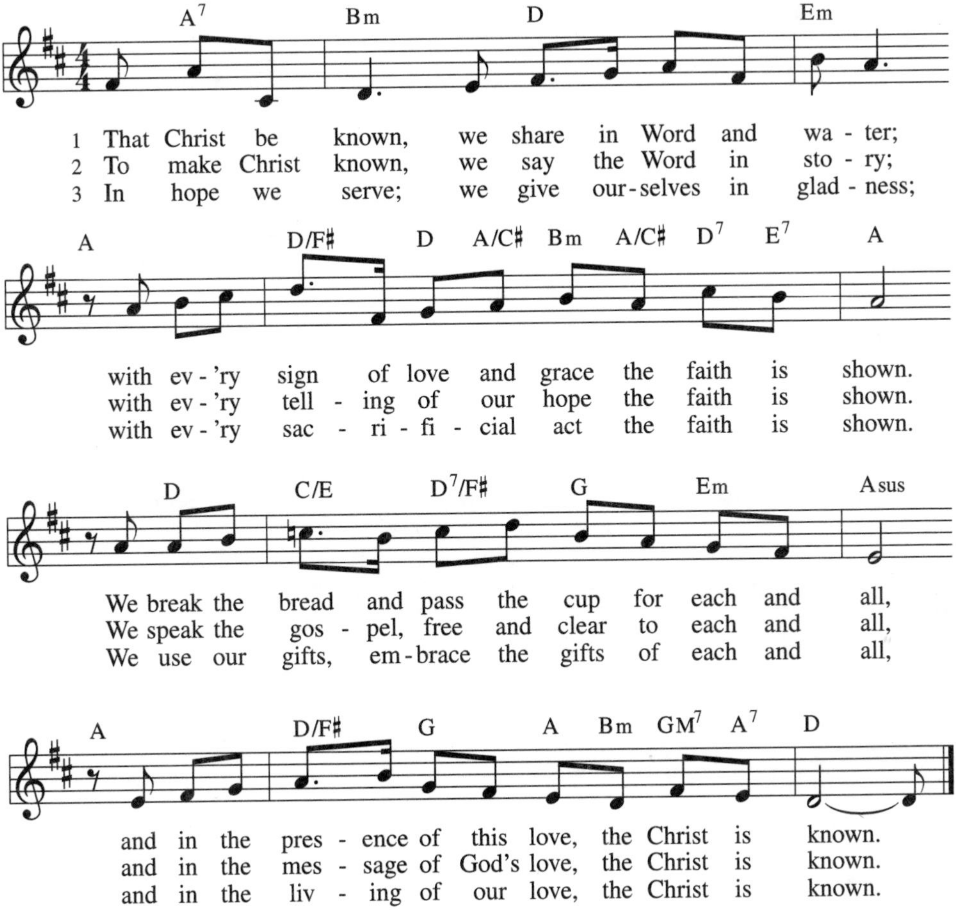

1 That Christ be known, we share in Word and wa - ter;
2 To make Christ known, we say the Word in sto - ry;
3 In hope we serve; we give our-selves in glad - ness;

with ev - 'ry sign of love and grace the faith is shown.
with ev - 'ry tell - ing of our hope the faith is shown.
with ev - 'ry sac - ri - fi - cial act the faith is shown.

We break the bread and pass the cup for each and all,
We speak the gos - pel, free and clear to each and all,
We use our gifts, em-brace the gifts of each and all,

and in the pres - ence of this love, the Christ is known.
and in the mes - sage of God's love, the Christ is known.
and in the liv - ing of our love, the Christ is known.

Text and music: Marty Schaefer

That we may be filled

F
B♭/F
F
B♭/F
Not as we ought but as we are a - ble, we
F/A
B♭
F/C
B♭
of - fer our thanks as we come to your ta - ble. Through
F/A
C/B♭ B♭
F/C
B♭m/D♭
Word and Spir - it bless us; through bread and wine re - fresh us that
F/C
B♭
F/A
Gm7
C7
F
we may be filled, that we may be filled with love.

Text: Handt Hanson and Paul Murakami
Music: Handt Hanson and Paul Murakami; arr. Henry Wiens

The church song
135
Refrain
We are the church, the body of our Lord;
we are all God's children. We have been restored.
1 The church is not a building where people go to pray;
it's not made out of sticks and stones, it's not made out of clay.
2 You can go to worship but you cannot go to church;
you can't find a building that's alive no matter how you search.
3 The church is not a business, a committee or a board;
it's not a corporation for the business of the Lord.
4 The church, it is the people living out their lives,
called, enlightened, sanctified for the work of Jesus Christ.
Refrain

Text and music: Jay Beech

136 The King of glory

Refrain
Em Bm7 Em
The King of glory comes, the nation rejoices.
Em Bm7 Em
Open the gates before him, lift up your voices.
G C Bm/D D7 G
1 Who is the King of glory; how shall we call him?
2 In all of Galilee, in city or village,
3 Sing then of David's Son, our Savior and brother;
4 He gave his life for us, the pledge of salvation;
5 He conquered sin and death; he truly has risen,
Em CM7 G/B CM7 D7 G
He is Emmanuel, the promised of ages.
he goes among his people, curing their illness.
in all of Galilee was never another.
he took upon himself the sins of the nation.
and he will share with us his heavenly vision.
Refrain

Text: Willard F. Jabusch
Music: Israeli traditional

137 The summons

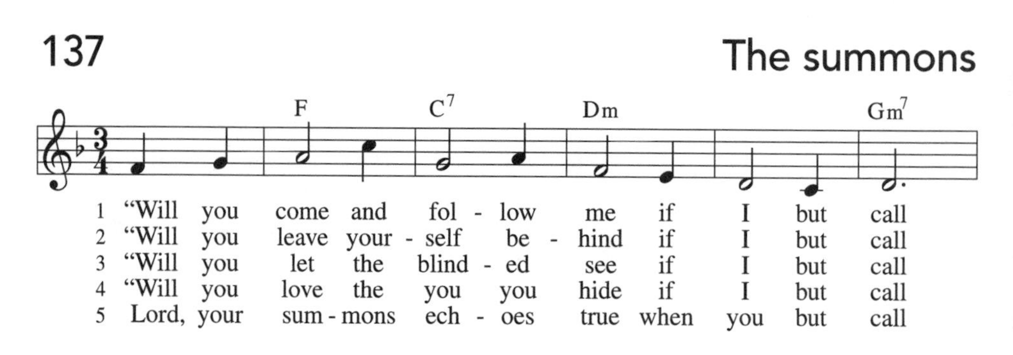
F C7 Dm Gm7
1 "Will you come and follow me if I but call
2 "Will you leave yourself behind if I but call
3 "Will you let the blinded see if I but call
4 "Will you love the you you hide if I but call
5 Lord, your summons echoes true when you but call

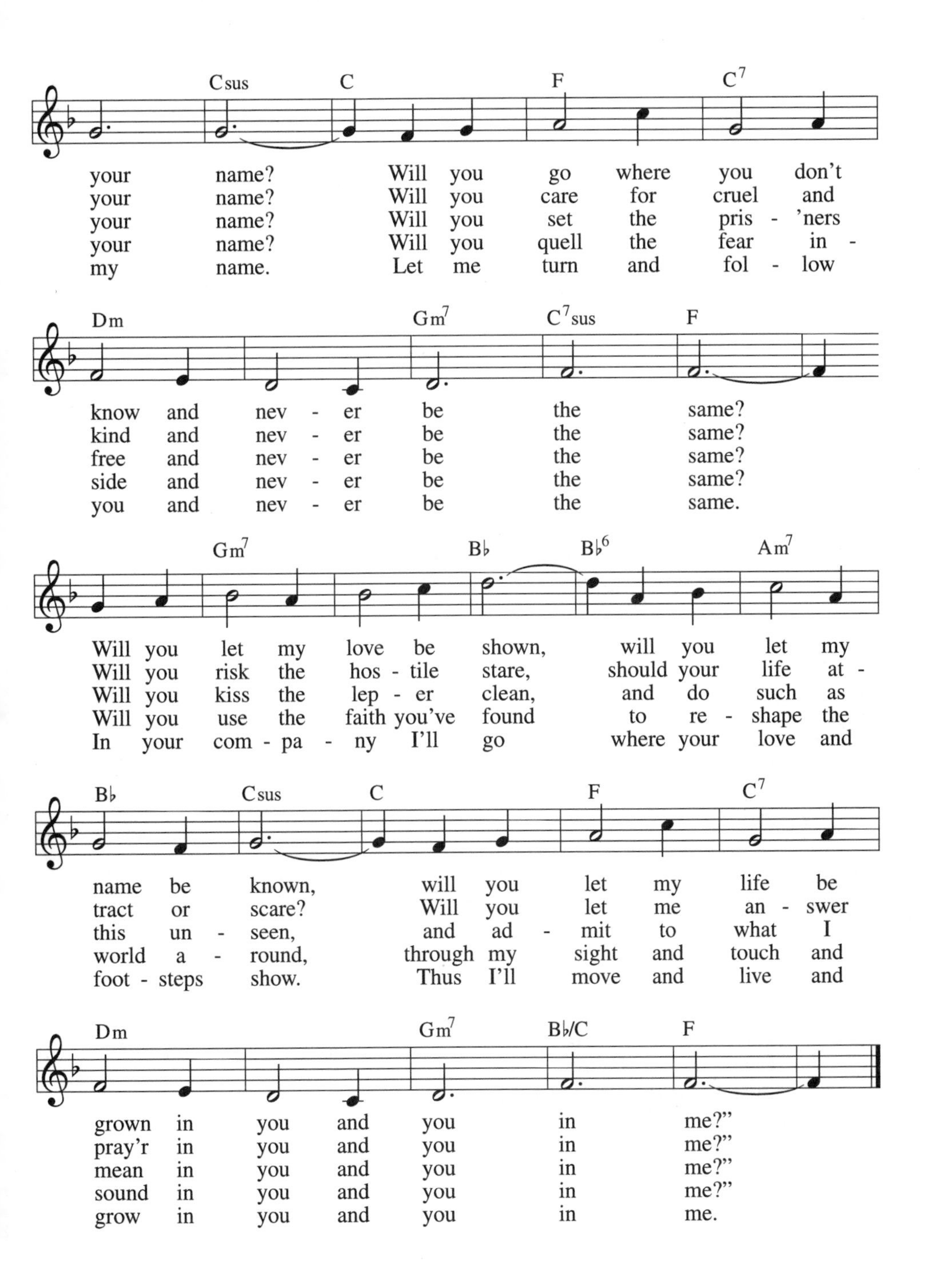
Csus C F C7
your name? Will you go where you don't
your name? Will you care for cruel and
your name? Will you set the pris - 'ners
your name? Will you quell the fear in -
my name. Let me turn and fol - low
Dm Gm7 C7sus F
know and nev - er be the same?
kind and nev - er be the same?
free and nev - er be the same?
side and nev - er be the same?
you and nev - er be the same.
Gm7 B♭ B♭6 Am7
Will you let my love be shown, will you let my
Will you risk the hos - tile stare, should your life at -
Will you kiss the lep - er clean, and do such as
Will you use the faith you've found to re - shape the
In your com - pa - ny I'll go where your love and
B♭ Csus C F C7
name be known, will you let my life be
tract or scare? Will you let me an - swer
this un - seen, and ad - mit to what I
world a - round, through my sight and touch and
foot - steps show. Thus I'll move and live and
Dm Gm7 B♭/C F
grown in you and you in me?"
pray'r in you and you in me?"
mean in you and you in me?"
sound in you and you in me?"
grow in you and you in me.

Text: John Bell
Music: Scottish traditional; arr. John Bell

138 The trees of the field

You shall go out with joy

Em
You shall go out with joy and be led forth with peace,
D G C G D B7
and the moun-tains and the hills will break forth be - fore you.
Em
There'll be shouts of joy and all the trees of the field
B7 Em/B B/A Em
will clap, will clap their hands.
D7 G C G D
And all the trees of the field will clap their hands.
G
The trees of the field will clap their hands.
C G D
The trees of the field will clap their hands,
B Am/C C♯dim B/D♯ Em
while you go out with joy.

Text: Steffi Geiser Rubin
Music: Stuart Dauermann

The trumpets sound, the angels sing

The feast is ready

1 The trum-pets sound, the an - gels sing, the feast is
2 Ta - bles are la - den with good things; oh, taste the
3 The hun-gry heart he sat - is - fies, of - fers the
read - y to be-gin. The gates of heav'n are o - pen wide,
peace and joy he brings. He'll fill you up with love di-vine;
poor his par - a-dise. Now hear all heav'n and earth ap-plaud
and Je - sus wel - comes you in - side.
he'll turn your wa - ter in - to wine.
the a - maz - ing good - ness of the Lord.
Refrain
Sing with thank-ful-ness songs of pure de-light. Come and rev-el in
heav-en's love and light. Take your place at the ta - ble of the King.
The feast is read - y to be-gin, the feast is read-y to be-gin.

Text and music: Graham Kendrick

There is a Redeemer

E♭ B♭/D E♭ A♭/C B♭7/D E♭ B♭/D E♭ A♭/C B♭ E♭ B♭
1 There is a Re - deem - er, Je - sus, God's own Son,
2 Je - sus, my Re - deem - er, name a - bove all names,
3 When I stand in glo - ry, I will see his face;
E♭ B♭/D E♭ A♭ E♭/G Fm7 B♭7sus E♭ A♭/B♭
pre - cious Lamb of God, Mes - si - ah, Ho - ly One.
pre - cious Lamb of God, Mes - si - ah, hope for sin - ners slain.
there I'll serve my king for - ev - er, in that ho - ly place.
Refrain
E♭sus2 E♭ Gm7 A♭ E♭/G Fm A♭/B♭ B♭7 E♭ B♭7sus B♭7
Thank you, O my Fa - ther, for giv - ing us your Son and
E♭ B♭/D E♭ A♭/C E♭/B♭ A♭ Fm7 B♭7sus B♭7 E♭
send - ing your Spir - it till the work on earth is done.

Text and music: Keith Green

This is the day

F
C7
This is the day, this is the day that the Lord has made, that the
Lord has made; we will re-joice, we will re-joice and be
F
B♭
glad in it, and be glad in it. This is the day that the
F
B♭
F
Lord has made; we will re-joice and be glad in it.
F/C
C7
F
This is the day, this is the day that the Lord has made.

Text: Psalm 118:24
Music: Les Garrett

142 This is the feast of victory

Refrain
D(no 3) A/C♯ Bm F♯m G F♯m
This is the feast of vic - to - ry for our God. Al - le - lu - ia.
E E7 Asus A Em7 Asus A
This is the feast of vic - to - ry. This is the feast of vic - to - ry for our
C G/B C G/B A/C♯ A Dsus D C9
God. Al - le - lu - ia, al - le - lu - ia.
A Em D C
1 Wor - thy is Christ, the Lamb who was slain, whose blood set us free to be peo-
G/B F C/E C
- ple of God. Pow - er, rich - es, wis - dom, and strength,
Am9 D7sus D7 G/B E7sus GM7/F♯ Asus A
hon - or and bless - ing, and glo - ry are his.
Refrain
D(no 3) A/C♯ Bm F♯m G F♯m
This is the feast of vic - to - ry for our God. Al - le - lu - ia.
E E7 Asus A Em7 Asus A
This is the feast of vic - to - ry. This is the feast of vic - to - ry for our
C G/B C G/B A/C♯ A Dsus D C9
God. Al - le - lu - ia, al - le - lu - ia.

A Em C
2 Sing with all the peo - ple of God, and join in the hymn of all cre -
G/B C G/B F C/E C
a - tion: Bless - ing, hon - or, glo - ry, and might
Am9 Dsus D G/B Am7 Esus E/F♯ G♯m7(♭5) Asus A7
be to God and the Lamb for - ev - er and ev - er. A - men.
Refrain
D(no 3) A/C♯ Bm F♯m G F♯m
This is the feast of vic - to - ry for our God. Al - le - lu - ia.
E E7 Asus A Em7 Asus A
This is the feast of vic - to - ry. This is the feast of vic - to - ry for our
C G/B C A/C♯ A Dsus D C9
God. Al - le - lu - ia, al - le - lu - ia.
A Em C
3 This is the feast of vic - to - ry for our God. Al - le - lu -
G/B G F/G C/G
ia. For the Lamb who was slain has be - gun his reign.
G Dm7/G G/F Esus F♯dim7 G♯dim7 Asus A7/E
Al - le - lu - ia, al - le - lu - ia.

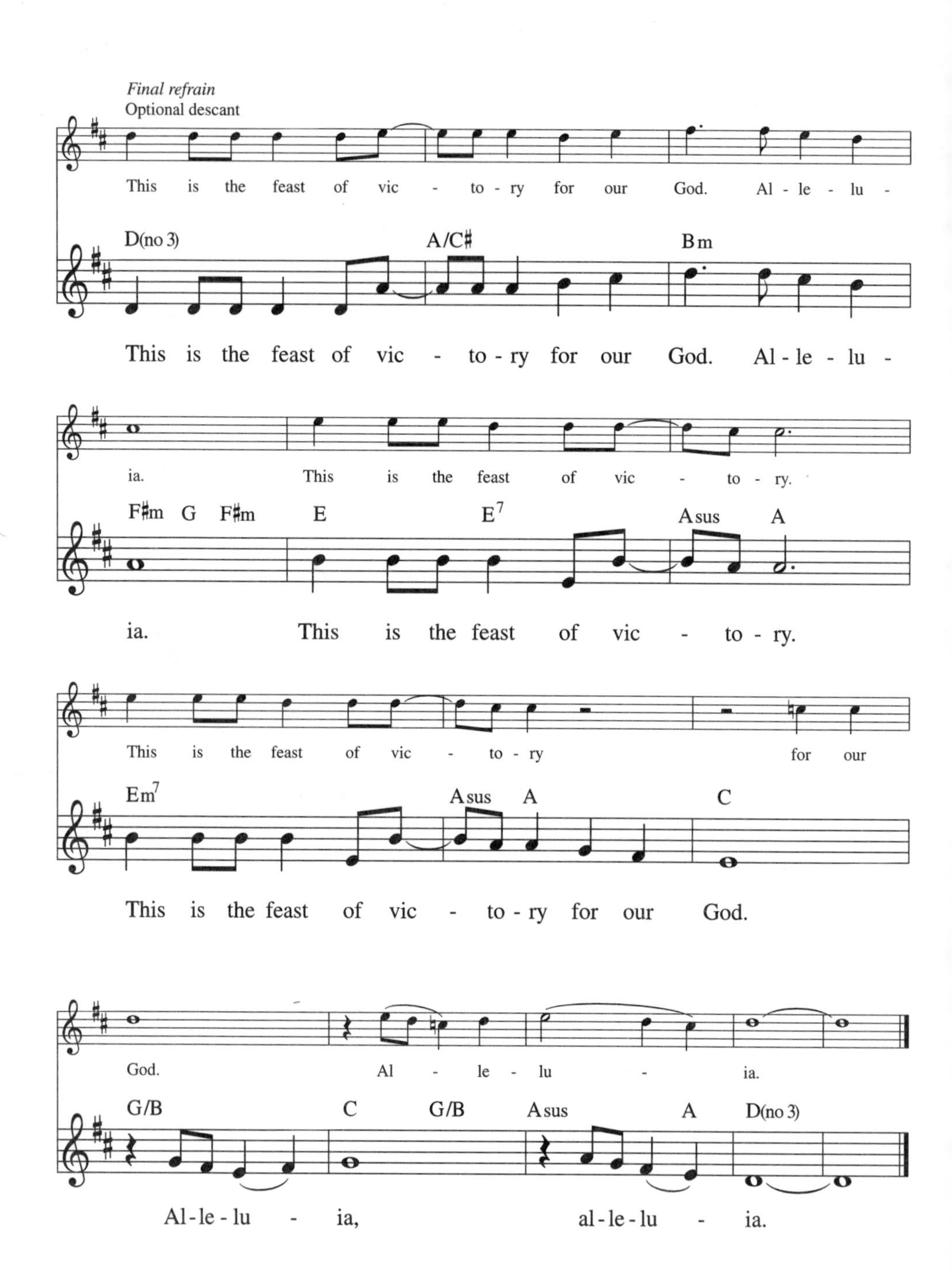
Final refrain
Optional descant
This is the feast of vic - to - ry for our God. Al - le - lu - ia.
This is the feast of vic - to - ry.
This is the feast of vic - to - ry for our God.
Al - le - lu - ia.
D(no 3) A/C♯ Bm
This is the feast of vic - to - ry for our God. Al - le - lu - ia.
F♯m G F♯m E E7 Asus A
This is the feast of vic - to - ry.
Em7 Asus A C
This is the feast of vic - to - ry for our God.
G/B C G/B Asus A D(no 3)
Al - le - lu - ia, al - le - lu - ia.

Text: John W. Arthur
Music: Jeremy Young

Thy word

Em D CM7 D Em D C
Thy word, thy word is a lamp un-to my feet.
Em D/F# Em7 D C Em
Thy word, oh, thy word is a lamp un-to my
D Am G D Em C
feet; and a light un-to my path, and a light un-to my
To repeat
Last time
D D Em C G
path. path, and a light un-to my path.

Text: Psalm 119:105
Music: Richard Webb

Thy word

Refrain
C7 F B♭ C7 F B♭ F
Thy word is a lamp un-to my feet and a light un-to my path.
C Gm Dm Am B♭ C
1 When I feel a-fraid, think I've lost my way, still you're there right be-
B♭/F F C Gm Dm Am
side me, and noth-ing will I fear as long as you are near.
B♭ C Dm D A/C♯ Csus C7 Refrain
Please be near me to the end.
C Gm Dm Am B♭ C
2 I will not for-get your love for me, and yet my heart for-ev-er is
B♭/F F C Gm Dm Am
wan-der-ing. Je-sus, be my guide and hold me to your side, and
B♭ C Dm D A/C♯ Csus C7 Refrain
I will love you to the end.

Text: Psalm 119:105, refrain; Michael W. Smith, stanzas
Music: Amy Grant

Waterlife
14
F2 C Dm7sus F2 C Dm7sus F2 C Dm7
1 Be - fore I can re-mem-ber the cov - e - nant was sealed
2 A sim - ple sweet be - gin - ning, a lov - ing place to start:
3 My hope and ex - pec - ta - tion for true com - mun - i - ty
F2 C Dm7sus F2 C Dm7
with Fa - ther, Son, and Spir - it, in wa - ter was re - vealed.
Christ be - gan the sing - ing that swells with - in my heart.
be - gins with res - ur - rec - tion, his death and life in me.
Gm F♯aug Gm/F B♭/C
The cleans - ing was for cer - tain, with wa - ter and the Word;
His love be - came my call - ing, his life my min - is - try.
His Spir - it fills the Bod - y: his church through wa - ter sees
F2 C Dm7 F2 C Dm7sus
gen - tle words were spo - ken, in heav - en they were heard.
His name is my a - dop - tion in - to his fam - i - ly.
prom - ise for to - mor - row, his wa - ter - life in me.
Refrain
Dm7sus F/G Gm7 F/C B♭/C
They were sing - ing wa - ter - life, be - gin - ning life,
FM7 C/D Dm7 C/D F/G Gm7
wa - ter - life all my life, wa - ter - life, Spir -
F/C B♭/C F2 C Dm7sus
- it life, wa - ter - life.
Last time
F2 C Dm7sus
wa - ter - life.

Text: Handt Hanson
Music: Handt Hanson, arr. Henry Wiens

We are an offering

G C2 Dm7 C2/E C/E
We lift our voic - es, we lift our hands, we lift our
F C/E Dm7 F/G G C2 Dm7
lives up to you: we are an of-fer-ing. Lord, use our voic-es, Lord, use our
C2/E C/E F C/E Dm7 F/G G/F
hands, Lord, use our lives, they are yours: we are an of-fer - ing.
Em7 Em7/A A Dm7 Dm7/G Esus D/F♯ E/G♯ Am
All that we have, all that we are, all that we hope to be, we
Dm7 C2/E B♭/C Dm7sus2 Dm7 F/G
give to you, we give to you.
G C2 Dm7 C2/E C/E
We lift our voic - es, we lift our hands, we lift our
F C/E Dm7 Dm7/G C
lives up to you: we are an of-fer-ing, we are an of-fer - ing.

Text and music: Dwight Liles

We are called

G G/B C C/D D
1 Come! Live in the light!
2 Come! O - pen your heart!
3 Sing! Sing a new song!
G G/B C D D/F♯
Shine with the joy and the love of the Lord! We are
Show your . . . mer - cy to all those in fear! We are
Sing of that great day when all will be one! God will
Em Em7/D C G/B
called to be light for the king - dom, to
called to be hope for the hope - less so all
reign, and we'll walk with each oth - er as
Am7 G/B C C/D D
live in the free - dom of the cit - y of God.
ha - tred and blind - ness will be . . . no more.
sis - ters and broth - ers u - nit - ed in love.
Refrain
Am9 G/B C D D/F♯ C/G D/G G G/B C
We are called to act with jus - tice, we are called to
D Em Em7/D G/B C D D/F♯
love ten - der - ly; we are called to serve one an -
C/G D/G G Am7 G/B C D C/G D/G G
oth - er, to walk hum - bly with God.

Text and music: David Haas

148 We are marching in the light of God

Siyahamba

We are marching in the light of God, we are marching in the light of God.
Si - ya - hamb' e - ku - kha - nyen' kwen - khos', si - ya - hamb' e - ku - kha - nyen' kwen - khos'.

We are marching in the light of God, we are marching in the light of God.
Si - ya - hamb' e - ku - kha - nyen' kwen - khos', si - ya - hamb' e - ku - kha - nyen' kwen - khos'.

we are marching in the light of, the light of God.
si - ya - hamb' e - ku - kha - nyen' kwen-, kha - nyen' kwen - khos'.

we are marching in the light of God.
si - ya - hamb' e - ku - kha - nyen' kwen - khos'.

We are marching oo
Si - ya - ham - ba oo

We are marching, marching, we are marching, marching,
Si - ya - ham - ba, ham - ba, si - ya - ham - ba, ham - ba,

we are march-ing in the light of God.
si-ya-hamb' e-ku-kha-nyen' kwen-khos'.
we are march-ing in the light of, the light of God.
si-ya-hamb' e-ku-kha-nyen' kwen-, kha-nyen' kwen-khos'.
we are march-ing in the light of God.
si-ya-hamb' e-ku-kha-nyen' kwen-khos'.
We are march-ing
Si-ya-ham-ba
oo
oo
We are march-ing, march-ing, we are march-ing, march-ing,
Si-ya-ham-ba, ham-ba, si-ya-ham-ba, ham-ba,
we are march-ing in the light of God.
si-ya-hamb' e-ku-kha-nyen' kwen-khos'.

Additional stanzas ad lib:

We are dancing…

We are praying…

We are singing…

Text: South African
Music: South African

149
We bow down
You are Lord of cre - a - tion and Lord of my life,
Lord of the land and the sea. You were Lord of the heav - ens be -
fore there was time, and Lord of all lords you will be.
We bow down and we wor - ship you, Lord; we bow
down and we wor - ship you, Lord; we bow down and we
wor - ship you, Lord; Lord of all lords you will be.

Text and music: Twila Paris

We bring the sacrifice of praise

150

D Em7 D2/F♯ G
We bring the sac - ri - fice of praise in - to the house of the
F♯m7 G/A D Em7 D2/F♯ Bm7
Lord; we bring the sac - ri - fice of praise in - to the
Em7 GM7/A A Dsus D D/F♯ G
house of the Lord. And we of - fer up to
F♯m7 Bm7 Em7 G/A A7 D Dsus/E D/F♯ D7
you the sac - ri - fic - es of thanks - giv - ing; and we
G F♯m7 Bm7 Em7 G/A A7 D
of - fer up to you the sac - ri - fic - es of joy.

Text and music: Kirk Dearman

151 We rejoice in the grace of God

A D E A F♯m D
We re-joice in the grace of God poured up-on our lives;
Esus E F♯m D E A
lov-ing-kind-ness has come to us be-
D G Esus E A D
cause of Je-sus Christ. We re-joice in the
E A F♯m F♯m/E B/D♯
grace of God, our hearts o-ver-flow.
D A/C♯ Bm7 E D A
What a joy to know the grace of God!

Text and music: Steve Cook and Vicki Cook

We remember you

C2 Dm7 F/G G C G/B Am
In bro - ken bread and the cup that we share, we re -
F FM7 Gsus G C2 Dm7
mem - ber you. In bro - ken bread and the
F/G G C G/B Am Dm7 G7 Csus C
cup that we share, we re - mem - ber you.
F G/F C/E Am CM7/G F
We re - mem-ber you, Je - sus. We re -
G C Am CM7/G F G F/A G/B
mem-ber your love for us. We re - mem - ber the
C G/B Am C/G F/G G7 C
blood you shed. We re - mem - ber you.

Text and music: Rick Founds

153

We see the Lord

Optional descant
We see Je - sus.
E A/B E
We see the Lord,
We see Je - sus.
A/E E
we see the Lord, and he is
High, he is high,
B7 E
high and lift - ed up, and his train fills the tem - ple. He is
he is high.
B7 E
high and lift - ed up, and his train fills the tem - ple. The
An - gels cry, "Ho - ly," the an - gels cry, "Ho - ly," the
A/E E A/E E
an - gels cry, "Ho - ly," the an - gels cry, "Ho - ly," the

an - gels cry, "Ho - ly is the Lord."
E/B B7 E A/E E
an - gels cry, "Ho - ly is the Lord."

Text: anonymous, based on Isaiah 6:1, 3
Music: anonymous; arr. Betty Pulkingham

We will glorify

154

D G A/E A D
1 We will glo - ri - fy the King of kings, we will
2 Lord Je - ho - vah reigns in maj - es - ty, we will
3 He is Lord of heav - en, Lord of earth, he is
4 Hal - le - lu - jah to the King of kings, hal - le -
G A/E A D G A/E A/C♯
glo - ri - fy the Lamb; we will glo - ri - fy the
bow be - fore his throne; we will wor - ship him in
Lord of all who live; he is Lord a - bove the
lu - jah to the Lamb; hal - le - lu - jah to the
Bm D/F♯ G D/A A D
Lord of lords, who is the great I AM.
righ - teous - ness, we will wor - ship him a - lone.
u - ni - verse, all praise to him we give.
Lord of lords, who is the great I AM.

Text: Twila Paris
Music: Twila Paris; arr. David Allen

155

What a mighty word God gives

D G D G
What a might - y Word God gives!
A/F♯ Bm7 Em7 A7sus A7
What a might - y Word God gives!
D G/A D G/E
When he speaks, our faith is fed. Give us, Lord, our dai - ly bread.
God sent us the on - ly Son, who for us the vic - try's won.
D/F♯ G D/A A7 D
What a might - y Word God gives!

Text: James Tallman
Music: anonymous

What have we to offer?

D A D
1 What have we to of - fer? What have we to share?
2 What have we to of - fer? What have we to bring?
3 What have we to of - fer? What have we to give?
G D Bm Asus A
Coins from the cof - fer, hearts filled with care.
Love, ripe with laugh - ter; hope that we can sing;
Eyes that are wide o - pen; lies that we won't live;
G D F# Bm G
God will not fal - ter; so let us dare
dreams of what we're af - ter; prom - is - es of when.
truth that must be spo - ken; jus - tice some - how.
D A D
lay it at the al - tar there.
Lay it at the al - tar then.
Lay it at the al - tar now.
D D/C# Bm7 G
4 What have we to of - fer? What have we to
Em7 Asus A D
give? Lives we will live.

Text and music: Ray Makeever

Wind of the Spirit

E/A E/G♯
Wind of the Spir - it, move fresh as we wor - ship and
F♯m A/B E
fill us with hope ev - 'ry day.
E/A E/G♯
Breath of cre - a - tion, blow life in our be - ing, and
F♯m A/B D
gift us with pur - pose, we pray; so our
G♯m7 F♯m/C♯ F♯m7 A/B
life is filled with mean - ing, and love is what we're breath-ing in the
E/A E/G♯ F♯m A/B E
wind of the Spir - it, wind of the Spir - it.

Text: Handt Hanson and Paul Murakami
Music: Handt Hanson and Paul Murakami; arr. Henry Wiens

158 You are mine

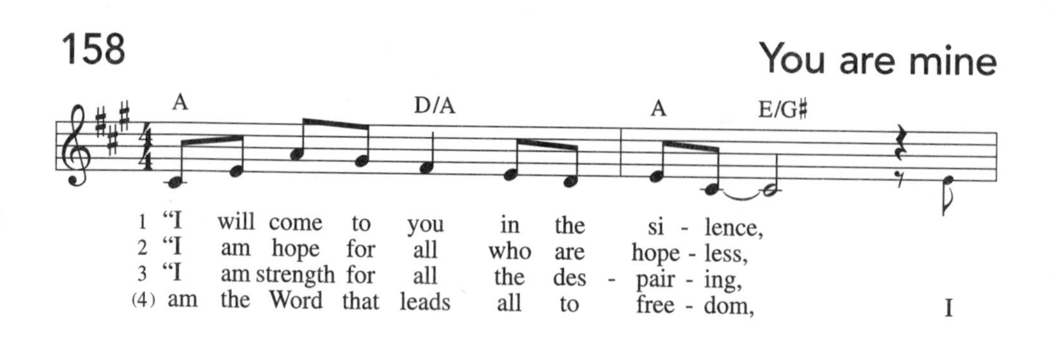
A D/A A E/G♯
1 "I will come to you in the si - lence,
2 "I am hope for all who are hope - less,
3 "I am strength for all the des - pair - ing,
(4) am the Word that leads all to free - dom, I

F♯m7 D Esus E
I will lift you from all your fear.
I am eyes for all who long to see. In the
heal - ing for the ones who dwell in shame.
am the peace the world can - not give.
A D/A C♯ C♯/E♯ F♯m
You will hear my voice, I claim you as my choice. Be
shad - ows of the night, I will be your light.
All the blind will see, the lame will all run free, and
I will call your name, em - brac - ing all your pain. Stand
Bm A/C♯ D Esus E Esus E
still and know I am here. (To stanza 2)
Come and rest in me. (To refrain)
all will know my name. (To refrain)
up, now walk and live! (To refrain)
Refrain
A D/A E/G♯ F♯m7 D
Do not be a - fraid, I am with you. I have called you each by
Esus E A D/A E/G♯ F♯m F♯m7/E
name. Come and fol - low me, I will bring you home; I
To stanzas
Last time
D Esus E A E/A D/A E/A A E/A D/A E/A A
love you and you are mine.” 4 “I

Text and music: David Haas

You are my God

E♭/F B♭ Cm7sus B♭/D B♭ B♭/E♭ E♭
You are my God, I am your ser - vant.
Cm7 F F/E♭ Dm7 Gm7 B♭/A♭ A♭
You are my King, my Lord and Sav - ior.
E♭/F B♭ Cm7sus B♭/D B♭ B♭/E♭ E♭
You are my friend, my joy and com - fort.
Gm E♭/G B♭/F E♭/F E♭/B♭ B♭ Dsus D/F♯
You are my Lord, you are my God.
Gm E♭ B♭ F Dm Gm E♭/G
Hear, hear the an - gels sing, all cre-a - tion bring you the
B♭/F F D/F♯ Gm E♭ B♭ F Dm
glo - ry. And I will lift my heart in faith, lift my eyes to
Gm B♭/D Cm7 B♭/D E♭ Gm Cm7 B♭/D
see you in ho - li - ness, in righ - teous -
E♭ Gm Cm7 B♭/D E♭/F E♭/B♭ B♭
ness, in maj - es - ty; you are my God.

Text and music: Geoff Bullock and Gail Dunshea

You are my hiding place

1*
Am Dm7 G G/B
You are my hid - ing place; you al - ways
Csus C G/B F/A Dm
fill my heart with songs of de - liv - er - ance. When-
Esus E 2 Am
ev - er I am a - fraid I will trust in you,
Dm7 G G/B C G/B
I will trust in you. Let the weak say,
F/A Dm To repeat Esus E
"I am strong in the strength of the Lord."
Last time Esus E Am
strength of the Lord, I will trust in you."

*may be sung in canon

Text and music: Michael Ledner

161
You are the rock of my salvation
Rock of my salvation
Fm9 Gm7 Cm B♭/C
You are the rock of my sal - va - tion,
A♭M7 B♭ Cm B♭/C Fm9 Gm7
you are the strength of my life. You are my hope and my in -
Cm B♭/C A♭M7 B♭ Cm
- spi - ra - tion; Lord, un - to you will I cry. I be -
A♭M7 B♭ Gm7 Cm7
lieve in you, be - lieve in you, for your
A♭M7 B♭ Cm7 B♭/C Cm7 A♭M7 B♭
faith - ful love to me. You have been my help in
Gm7 Cm7 Fm Fm/A♭ Gsus G
time of need; Lord, un - to you will I cleave.
Fm9 Gm7 Cm B♭/C
You are the rock of my sal - va - tion,
A♭M7 B♭ Cm
you are the strength of my life.

Text and music: Teresa Muller

You, Lord

F/G G C/G F/G C/E Dm7
We stand here in awe be-fore you, Lord.
C C/G F/G C/E Dm7
We kneel here and hon - or you, Lord,
C G/B Am7 F C/G G♯dim7
for love nev - er end-ing, for grace free-ly
Am FM9 F/G C
giv - ing. We come here to thank you, Lord.
C/F F G/F Em
It's you, Lord, on - ly you, Lord:
G/A Am Dm7 F/G G C
to you we bring this of - fer - ing of praise.
B♭/C C C/F F G/F Em
It's you, Lord, on - ly you, Lord:
G/A Am Dm7 C/E F
ev - 'ry - thing I give; my life I want to
F/G C
live for you, Lord.

Text: Handt Hanson
Music: Handt Hanson; arr. Henry Wiens

Acknowledgments

Consultants and contributors are gratefully acknowledged: Jay Beech, Marshall Bowen, Robin Cain, Dori Erwin Collins, Robert Buckley Farlee, Mark Glaeser, Rob Glover, Heidi Hagstrom, Handt Hanson, Ben Houge, David Householder, David Jahn, Phil Kadidlo, Dean Krippaehne, Terri McLean, Ralph C. Sappington, John Ylvisaker, Jeremy Young

Additional reviewers are gratefully acknowledged: Katie Adelman, Arletta Anderson, Kevin Anderson, Carole Lea Arenson, Donald M. Brandt, Linda Bronstein, Lorraine Brugh, Bill Çhouinard, Richard Colligan, William Eaton, Rusty Edwards, Steven B. Eulberg, Donna J. Hackler, Dave Janzer, Jeff Kjellberg, Dale Olson, Larry Olson, Karen Reynolds, Marty Schaefer, Kris Simon, Cathy Skogen-Soldner, Phil Spencer, James Tallman, David Tryggestad, Kathy Donlan Tunseth, Scott Tunseth, Erik Whitehill, Tim Wright, Michael Zehnder

ELCA publishing house and churchwide staff: Norma Aamodt-Nelson, Ruth Allin, Suzanne Burke, Katherine Carter, D. Foy Christopherson, Ann Delgehausen, Ryan French, Lynn Joyce Hunter, Lynette Johnson, Aaron Koelman, Rebecca Lowe, David Meyer, Paul Nelson, Kristine Oberg, Linda Parriott, Rachel Riensche, Douglas Schmitz, Ted Schroeder, Martin A. Seltz, Frank Stoldt, Eric Vollen, Karen Ward, Scott Weidler, Richard Webb, Mark Weiler, Eileen Zahn

Cover art and design: Greg Lewis Studios

Music engraving and preparation: Thomas Schaller, Mensura Music Preparation; Becky Brantner-Christiansen, J. David Moore

Copyright holders and administrators

A.P. WATT, LTD.
20 John Street
London WC1N 2DR UK
011-44-71-405-6774
011-44-71-831 2154 FAX

AUGSBURG FORTRESS
PO Box 1209
Minneapolis, MN 55440-1209
(800) 426-0115
(612) 330-3252 FAX

BEECH, JAY
c/o Baytone Music
1330 8th Ave. N., Suite 102
Moorhead, MN 56560
(218) 291-1386

BMG MUSIC PUBLISHING
One Music Circle North
Nashville, TN 37203-4310
(615) 780-5420

BRENTWOOD-BENSON MUSIC PUBLISHING
365 Great Circle Road
Nashville, TN 37228
(615) 742-6800
(615) 742-6950 FAX

C.A. MUSIC
c/o Music Services
Franklin, TN 37069
(615) 794-9015
(615) 794-0793 FAX

CHANGING CHURCH, INC.
200 East Nicollet Blvd
Burnsville, MN 55337-4521
(612) 435-8107

THE COPYRIGHT CO.
40 Music Square East
Nashville, TN 37203
(615) 244-5588
(615) 244-5591 FAX

DAKOTA ROAD MUSIC
PO Box 90344
Sioux Falls, SD 57109
(605) 362-9554

DAVID HIGHAM ASSOCIATES, LTD.
5-8 Lower John Street
Golden Square
London W1R 4HA UK
011-44-71-437-7888
011-44-71-437-1072 FAX

EKKLESIA MUSIC
PO Box 22967
Denver, CO 80222
(303) 757-4853

EMI CHRISTIAN MUSIC PUBLISHING
101 Winners Circle
Brentwood, TN 37024-5085
(615) 371-4400
(615) 371-6897 FAX

GAITHER MUSIC MANAGEMENT
PO Box 737
1703 S. Park Avenue
Alexandria, IN 46001
(765) 724-8233
(765) 724-8290 FAX

GIA PUBLICATIONS, INC.
7404 South Mason Avenue
Chicago, IL 60638
(800) 442-1358
(708) 496-3828 FAX

HOPE PUBLISHING CO.
380 South Main Place
Carol Stream, IL 60188
(800) 323-1049
(630) 665-2552 FAX

INTEGRITY MUSIC, INC.
1000 Cody Road
Mobile, AL 36695
(334) 633-9000
(334) 633-5202 FAX

KEVIN MAYHEW PUBLISHERS
Buxhall, Stowmarket
Suffolk IP14 3DJ UK
011-44-973-7978
011-44-973-7834 FAX

THE LORENZ CORP.
Box 802
Dayton, OH 45401-0802
(800) 444-1144
(513) 223-2042 FAX

MANNA MUSIC, INC.
35255 Brooten Road
PO Box 218
Pacific City, OR 97135
(503) 965-6112
(503) 965-6880 FAX

MUSIC SERVICES
209 Chapelwood Dr.
Franklin, TN 37069
(615) 794-9015
(615) 794-0793 FAX

NEW DAWN MUSIC
PO Box 18030
Portland, OR 97213-0248
(800) 548-8749
(503) 282-3486 FAX

OCP PUBLICATIONS
PO Box 18030
Portland, OR 97213-0248
(800) 548-8749
(503) 282-3486 FAX

PRINCE OF PEACE PUBLISHING
See Changing Church, Inc.

ROCKSMITH MUSIC
c/o Trust Music Management, Inc.
PO Box 22274
Carmel, CA 93922
(831) 626-1030
(831) 626-1026 FAX

SELAH PUBLISHING CO.
58 Pearl Street
Kingston, NY 12401-0902
(914) 338-2816
(914) 338-2991 FAX

SOVEREIGN MUSIC UK
PO Box 356
Leighton Buzzard
Bedfordshire LU 7 8 WP UK
011-44-52-538-5578
011-44-52-537-2743 FAX

YLVISAKER, JOHN
New Generation Publishers, Inc.
Box 321
Waverly, IA 50677-0321
(319) 352-0765

UNICHAPPELL MUSIC, INC.
c/o Hal Leonard Corp.
7777 West Bluemound Road
PO Box 13819
Milwaukee, WI 53213-0819
(414) 774-3630
(414) 774-3259 FAX

WALTON MUSIC CORP.
170 NE 33rd Street
Fort Lauderdale, FL 33334
(305) 563-1844

WORD MUSIC, INC.
c/o Acuff-Rose Music Publishing, Inc.
65 Music Square West
Nashville, TN 37203
(615) 321-5000
(615) 327-0560 FAX

Topics and themes

An expanded index of topics and themes appears in Worship & Praise *Full Music Edition.*

Scripture references

An expanded index of scripture references appears in Worship & Praise *Full Music Edition.*

Authors, composers, and sources

Titles and first lines

ISBN 0-8066-3850-8

9 780806 638508
90000